Fresh Sounds

COMPANION VOLUME TO 'SOUND OF LIVING WATERS'

compiled by

BETTY PULKINGHAM

and

JEANNE HARPER

D1510905

HODDER AND STOUGHTON

LONDON SYDNEY AUCKLAND TORONTO

Processed by Cambridge Music Printing Services, Cambridge.

Contents

Foreword

The flow of new songs as God's Spirit renews his Church today is such that no printing press can hope to keep pace. We offer a second *Sound of Living Waters* under a new title, *Fresh Sounds,* to convey the freshness of many new songs; they have already delighted Christians in different areas, and we trust will be your joy also.

There is in addition an exchange of good hymns from both sides of the Atlantic as in Book 1, set alongside songs of recent popularity such as *Sing to the Lord a new song,* a theme song from an international conference in Rome, and *Moto,* an enthusiastic song from East Africa.

The sections are headed in almost the same way as Book 1. Instead of *Songs for a season* and *Sing a Psalm* we have a liturgical section. In this section alone we find ample illustration of the breadth of the musical taste of the Holy Spirit. Passing from the gentle introit *Allelu* we are invited to *Come and dine* in a rousing American song; a serenely beautiful setting of the *Nunc Dimittis* is included here, and then the *Doxology* from the musical *Come Together.*

We invite you to explore some of the infinite variety and musical resourcefulness of God's creative Spirit and to expect him to use you as a vehicle for his power and praise as you sing, that others may hear and follow on to know for themselves his creativity and blessing.

BETTY PULKINGHAM AND JEANNE HARPER
1976

Acknowledgments

The editors are tremendously indebted to Mimi Farra for her gifts of precision and musicianship made available to us unreservedly. We wish to thank Gary Miles for his help in proof reading and copying, Mary Felton for her loyal secretarial service to us, Michael Wood for helping us to think clearly about the business procedures involved, and the Watkins family whose home we invaded many times because it afforded us a quiet and encouraging place to work. We are grateful to members of the Community of Celebration at Yeldall Manor in Berkshire, and the Cathedral of the Isles, Cumbrae, Scotland, for their hidden helpfulness in ways too numerous to mention.

Last of all we want to thank the *Fisherfolk* who have sung, taught, experimented with, improved upon and shared many of these songs throughout the Christian world. For indeed it is through their ministry that many in the church have come to hear *fresh sounds.*

SECTION 1

HALLELUJAH!

SONGS OF PRAISE AND THANKSGIVING

1. 'Sanna

Traditional
Arr. Betty Pulkingham

With fervency of expression
'San-na,* san-na-ni-na, san-na, san-na, san-na,
san - na, san-na, san - na, san-na-ni-na,
san - na, san - na, san - na.
San-
1.
2.

*This is a shortened form of the word 'hosanna.'

This song may be sung most effectively by voices in four-part harmony, unaccompanied.

2. Hail to the Lord's anointed

Based on Psalm 72
James Montgomery

'Yeldall'
Betty Pulkingham

Bright and well-accented

D
Am7
D
Am7
D
A
D
1. Hail to the Lord's a - noint - ed, Great Da - vid's
Hail in the time ap - point - ed, His reign on
2. He shall come down like show - ers Up - on the
And love, joy, hope, like flow - ers, Spring in his
C
A7
D
great-er Son!
earth be - gun! He comes to break op-
fruit-ful earth,
path to birth: Be-fore him on the
Am7
F
A7
pres - sion, To set the cap - tive free;
moun-tains Shall peace, the her - ald go;
8

D Em A D D Maj7 Am7
To take a - way trans - gres - sion, And rule
And right - eous - ness in foun - tains From hill
D Am7 D.S. D final ending
in e - qui - ty.
to val - ley flow.

3. Kings shall bow down before him,
   And gold and incense bring;
All nations shall adore him,
   His praise all people sing;
For he shall have dominion
   O'er every sea and shore;
His kingdom still increasing,
   A kingdom for evermore.

4. O'er every foe victorious,
   He on his throne shall rest;
From age to age more glorious,
   All blessing and all-blest:
The tide of time shall never
   His covenant remove;
His name shall stand for ever,
   His changeless name of love.

3. Crown him with many crowns

Matthew Bridges
Godfrey Thring
'Diademata'
George Job Elvey
Descant by Betty Pulkingham
With vigour
Descant
3. Crown him with ma - ny — crowns, — Who tri - umphed o'er the grave, — And — rose vic - to - rious for those — he — came to save, — His glo - ries, his
5. Crown him the Lord — of — heav'n, — En- throned in worlds a - bove, — Crown — him the King to whom is giv'n — the — name of love, — Crown him, — crown
1. Crown him with ma - ny crowns, The lamb up - on his throne; Hark! how the heav'n - ly an - them drowns All mu - sic but its own; A - wake, my soul, and
2. Crown him the Son of God Be - fore the worlds be- gan, And ye, who tread where he hath — trod, Crown him the Son of man; Who ev' - ry grief hath
3. Crown him the Lord of life, Who tri-umphed o'er the grave, And rose vic - to - rious in the — strife For those he came to save; His glo - ries now we

glo - ries now — we sing, Who died e - ter - nal
him with ma - ny crowns, As thrones be - fore — him
sing Of him who died for thee, And
known That wrings the hu - man breast, And
sing Who died, and rose on high, Who
life — to bring — and lives that death may die.
fall, — crown him, — for he is Lord - of all.
hail him as thy match - less King Through all e - ter - ni - ty.
takes and bears them for his own, That all in him may rest.
died, e - ter - nal life to bring, And lives that death may die.

4. Crown him of lords the Lord,
 Who over all doth reign,
Who once on earth, the incarnate Word,
 For ransomed sinners slain,
Now lives in realms of light,
 Where saints with angels sing
Their songs before him day and night,
 Their God, Redeemer, King.

5. Crown him the Lord of heav'n,
 Enthroned in worlds above;
Crown him the King, to whom is giv'n
 The wondrous name of Love.
Crown him with many crowns,
 As thrones before him fall,
Crown him, ye kings, with many crowns,
 For he is King of all.

4. The God of Abraham praise

Jewish Doxology
Para. Thomas Olivers
'Leoni'
Arr. Meyer Lyon
Descant by Betty Pulkingham
With vigour
(Descant) 5. The whole tri - umph-ant host give thanks to
God on high, 'Hail Fa - - - ther, Son and
Ho - ly Ghost,' they cry. Hail A - bra-ham's God and
1. The God of A- braham praise, Who reigns en -throned a-
2. He by him - self hath sworn: I on his oath de-
3. There dwells the Lord, our King, The Lord, our right - eous-
bove; An - cient of ev - er - last - ing days, And
pend; I shall, on ea - gle wings up - borne, To
ness, Tri - umph - ant o'er the world and sin, The
God of love; To him up - lift your
heav'n as - cend: I shall be - hold his
Prince of peace; On Si - on's sa - cred

mine, we join the heav'n-ly lays, All might and
voice, At whose supreme com - mand, From earth we rise, and
face, I shall his power a - dore, And sing the won-ders
height His king - dom he main - tains, And, glo -rious with his
ma - jes - ty, and end- less praise.. A - - - - - - - - - - -men.
seek the joys At his right hand.
of his grace For - ev - - - - er - more.
saints in light, For - ev - - - - er reigns.
A - - - - - - - - - - men.

4. The God who reigns on high
 The great archangels sing,
And 'Holy, holy, holy', cry,
 Almighty King!
Who was, and is, the same,
 And evermore shall be:
Eternal Father, great I AM,
 We worship thee.

5. The whole triumphant host
 Give thanks to God on high;
'Hail, Father, Son and Holy Ghost!'
 They ever cry;
Hail, Abraham's God and mine!
 I join the heav'nly lays;
All might and majesty are thine,
 And endless praise.

5. Hallelujah! Gonna sing all about it

Roy Turner
Arr. Betty Pulkingham

With a bounce
E
E7
Hal - le - lu - jah! Gon - na sing all a-bout it. Hal - le-
A
E
lu - jah! Gon - na shout all a-bout it. Hal - le - lu - jah! Can't
B7
E
(Praise God)
live with-out it, praise God. Now I'm liv - ing in a
Ped.
E7
A
new cre - a - tion, now I'm drink - ing at the well of sal - va - tion.
E
A
E
A
E
Now there is no con - dem - na - tion, praise God. (Praise God.)

6. Hallelujah, my Father

Tim Cullen

With quiet devotion
Hal-le - lu - jah, my— Fa - - ther,— for— giv-ing us your
Son; send-ing him— in - to— the world to be giv-en up for
men, know - ing— we would bruise him— and smite him from the
earth. Hal-le - lu - jah, my— Fa - - ther,— in his
death is my birth.— Hal-le - lu - jah, my—

Fa - - ther, in his life is my life.

7. Praise my God with the tambourine

Adapted from Judith 16: 1, 13-19
Jerusalem Bible

Diane Davis

Boldly, with vigour

Refrain

Am Em Am

Praise my God with the tam - bou - rine; Sing to the Lord with the

Em Am 1. Am 2. *Fine*

cym - - - - - - - bals. - bals.

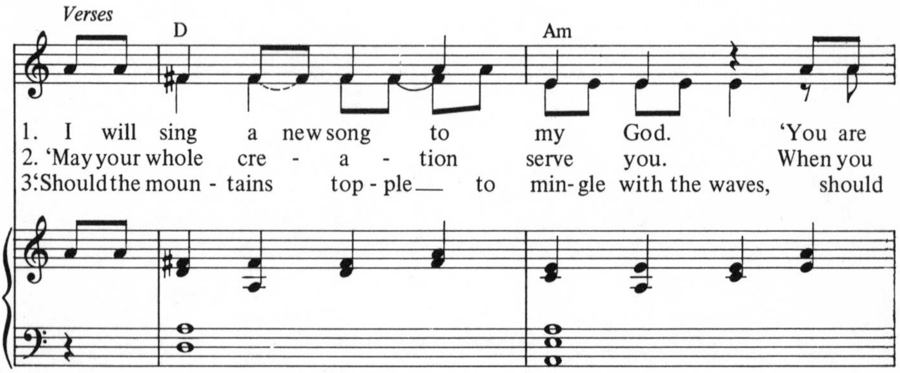

Verses

D Am

1. I will sing a new song to my God. 'You are
2. 'May your whole cre - a - tion serve you. When you
3. 'Should the moun - tains top - ple to min - gle with the waves, should

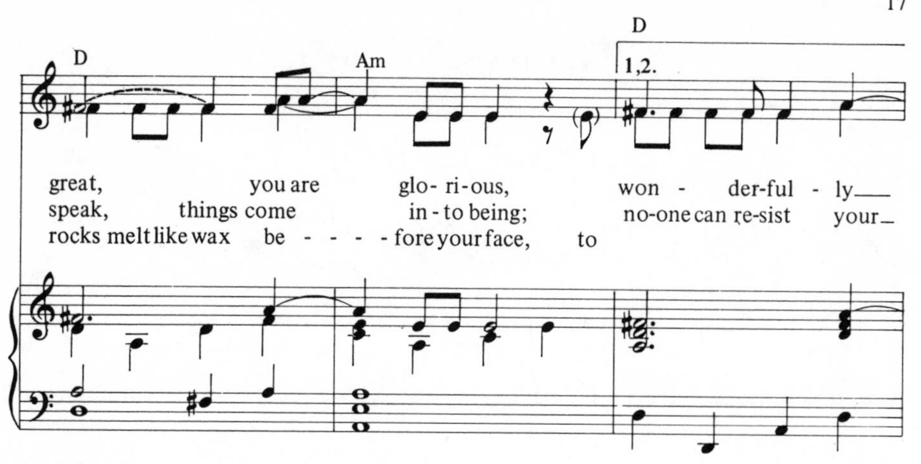
D
Am
D
1,2.
great, you are glo- ri-ous, won - der-ful - ly
speak, things come in - to being; no-one can re-sist your
rocks melt like wax be - - - - fore your face, to

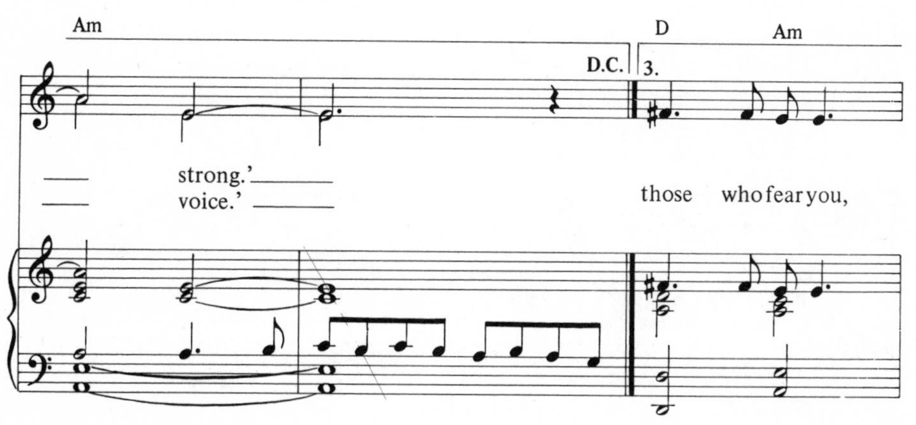
Am
D
Am
D.C.
3.
strong.'
voice.'
those who fear you,

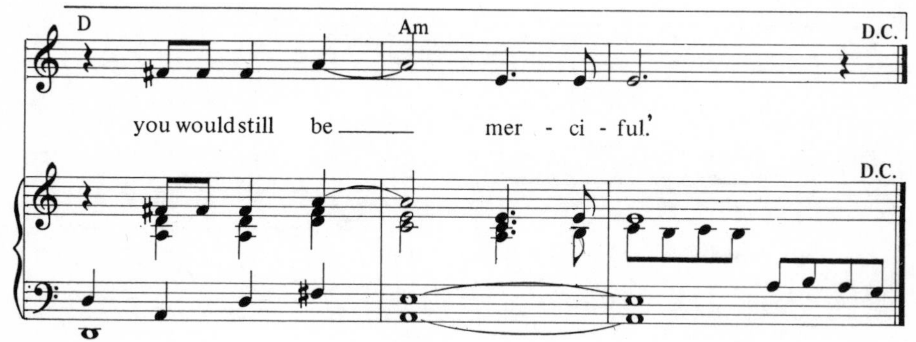
D
Am
D.C.
you would still be mer - ci - ful.'
D.C.

8. The dancing heart

Roy Turner
Arr. Betty Pulkingham

With joyful abandon
D
A7
1. Da - vid danced be - fore the Lord, he danced with all his might; his
D
heart was filled with ho - ly joy, his spi - rit was so light.
G
Mi - chal through the win - dow looked, to cri - ti - cise did start, she
A7
D
Refrain
A7
did - n't know that Da - vid had got a danc-ing heart. Oh, the
D
A
Ho - ly Ghost will set your feet a - danc - ing! The

(Hal - le - lu - jah)
A
D
Ho - ly Ghost will fill you through and through. The
G
Ho - ly Ghost will set your feet a - danc - ing, and
A
A7
D
set your heart a - danc - ing too!

2. David danced before the Lord to magnify his name;
In God's almighty presence he felt no sense of shame;
The oil of gladness flowed that day, it quickened every part;
He hadn't only dancing feet, he had a dancing heart.

3. Out of Egypt long ago the Israelites were led;
By a mighty miracle they all were kept and fed;
Through the Red sea they were brought, the waters stood apart,
And God gave sister Miriam a dance down in her heart.

4. There was a celebration - upon the Red sea shore;
Timbrels rang, desert sands became a dancing floor;
The people sang and praised God there, he made the gloom depart.
And put a dance of love and joy a-deep down in their hearts.

5. The prodigal was far away - wandering out in sin,
But he came back to father's house and father took him in;
He put a robe upon his son - the merriment did start,
The prodigal got dancing shoes to match his dancing heart.

6. The father's house with music rang to welcome home the son;
Wine was flowing full and free, all misery was gone;
The elder brother looking on complained it wasn't fair;
He hadn't got a dancing heart like all the others there.

7. Now many saints are cold and bound by unbelief today,
They want the blessings of the Lord but worry what men say;
Oh, let the Lord have full control, from dead traditions part,
And he will set you free within, you'll have a dancing heart.

9. Now let us sing

Traditional
Arr. Betty Pulkingham

With a swing
A
Sing 'til the pow'r of the Lord comes down.
Now let us sing.
Now let us sing.
E
Sing 'til the pow'r of the Lord comes down.
Lift up your hands,
A
Lift up your hands,
D
don't be a - fraid. Now let us
don't be a - fraid.
A
E
Fine
A
sing 'til the pow'r of the Lord comes down.
sing 'til the pow'r of the Lord comes down. Now let us sing.

Possible variations:

Now let us (praise, pray, love.......) *or*
Lift up your (hearts, heads.......)

10. Sing praise to the Lord forever

'Jacob's Song'

Capo 4 (C)

Jacob Krieger
Adapted by Mikel Kennedy

With strength, briskly

Refrain
E(C)
A(F)
B(G)
(Part1) Sing praise to the Lord for - ev - er and ev -
(Part 2) Sing

E(C)
A(F)
B(G)
er.
praise to the Lord for - ev - er and ev -

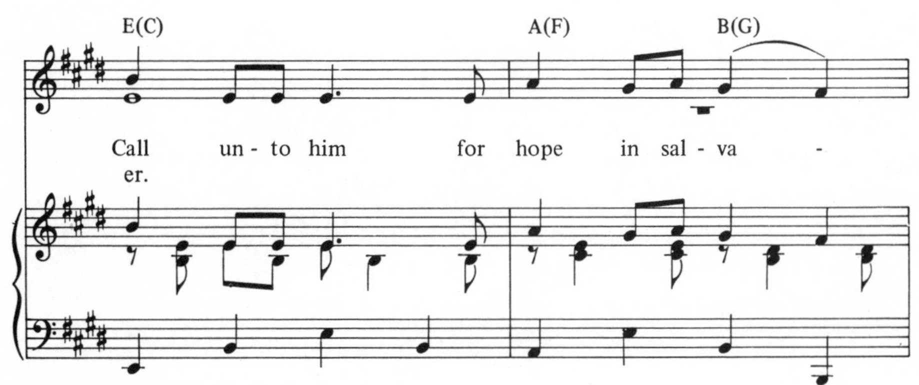
E(C)
A(F)
B(G)
Call un - to him for hope in sal - va -
er.

E(C)
A(F)
B(G)
tion.
Call un - to him for hope in sal va -
E(C)
A(F)
E(C)
B(G)
E(C)
tion. Sing praise, al - le - lu - ia, sing praise, al - le - lu! Sing
A(F)
E(C)
last time
B(G)
E(C)
praise, al - le - lu - ia, sing praise, al - le - lu!
C#m(Am)
B(G)
C#m(Am)
1. Oh, sing praise to our Fa - ther in
2. Oh, sing praise to the Son of
3. Oh, sing praise to the Spi - rit of

B(G)
C♯m(Am)
F♯(D)
heav'n. Sing un - to the
God. Call un - to his
God. Sing to the Lord of
B(G)
B7(G7)
D.S.
A(F)
E(C)
Lord.
name.
life.
Sing praise, al - le - lu! Sing
praise, al - le - lu! Sing
D.S.
Broaden
A(F)
E(C)
B(G)
E(C)
praise, al - le - lu - ia, sing praise, al - le - lu!

11. Sing, sing alleluia

Capo 2 (Am)

Nancy Carr Newman

Joyously
Bm(Am)
A(G)
Bm(Am)
Refrain
Bm(Am)
A(G)
Bm(Am)
Sing, sing al - le - lu - ia, sing
Emsus2 (Dmsus2)
Em(Dm)
F♯7(E7)
glo - - - - - - ry Je - sus Christ.
Bm(Am)
A(G)
Bm(Am)
Sing, sing al - le - lu - ia, be-
Em7(Dm7)
Bm(Am)
last time
hold the Lamb of God.

Em(Dm)
Bm(Am)
Em(Dm)
3
Bm(Am)
1. He rules the heavens, master of the earth.
3. place your trust in him.
2. Who is the King of glory? What is his name?
3. Come ye who seek the Lord,
G(F)
D(C)
F♯7(E7)
D.S.
1. All men now join together to praise the Lord.
3. Jesus will set you free to follow him.
D.S.
2. Jesus of Nazareth is his name.
D.S.
Bm(Am)
A(G)
Bm(Am)
A(G)
Bm(Am)
(Part 1) Sing, sing alleluia.
2nd time
All
(lu - ia.) (Part 2) Sing, sing alleluia.
Optional descant for refrain
Sing, sing, sing alleluia, sing glory Jesus Christ.
Sing, sing, sing alleluia, behold the Lamb of God.

12. Sing to the Lord

Donald Fishel
Arr. Betty Pulkingham

Strongly accented
C
f
Sing to the Lord a new song,
Am
sing to the Lord a new song,
F
sing to the Lord, sing
Dm
to the Lord a new
G
last time
song.
C
Am
1. God made the world in sev - en days.
2. God said to Mo - ses, 'Go and set my peo - ple free.
3. Je - sus said to Pe - ter, 'Come on, I'm call - ing you. I
4. Come on my bro - ther, won't you turn to Je - sus now, he

C
Am
A - dam sinn'd and then all men fell a - way.
I will be your guide, just al - ways fol - low me.'
know the way is hard, but I'll al - ways see you through.'
knows that you're a sin - ner but he loves you an - y - how.
C
Am
Je - sus came to re - deem my soul. He
Mo - ses led the peo - ple through the part - ed Red Sea, then they
Pe - ter said, 'My Lord, I'm a sin - ful man.' Then he
Je - sus paid the price for your sal - va - tion, just
F
G
died up - on the cross and he made me whole!
sang, and they danced, and they had a jub - i - lee!
threw down his net, and to the Lord he ran!
call up - on his name and you're a new cre - a - - - tion!
cresc.
last time
F
Dm
C
sing to the Lord a new song.

13. We will sing to the Lord our God

Richard Gullen

With rhythmic drive
Refrain
G C G F C G
f We will sing to the Lord our God,
F C G
might - y and splen - did is he!
We will
C G F C G
sing to our Sa - viour and King,
last time
F C G
1. 2.
glo - ri - ous in ma - jes - ty.
We will

F
mp
A
G
1. Here is the Lord, he is a - mong us;
mp
2. Here is the Lord, let us walk with him;
mp
F
A
G
let us wor - ship him to - geth - er.
he will lead and guide us through his land.
F
Am
Here is the Lord, he is a-mong
Here is the Lord, let us

G
F
us;
let us
walk with him;
we will

C
G
cresc.
D.S.
praise him all to-geth - er.
We will
D.S.
walk in peace through-out his land.
We will
D.S.
cresc.

F
C
G
Glo-ri-ous in ma - jes-ty.

14. This is the day of the Lord

Charles High

Liltingly

S A

This is the day— of the Lord. This is the day— of the

T B

Lord. ——
This is the day— of the

Lord. —— Al - le - lu, — al - le - lu.

A good song for unaccompanied singing, using only 'fingertip' clapping (the fingertips of the right hand against the palm of the left.)

Adapt verses to suit occasion, such as:

1. This is the (feast.....birthday.....service.....song) of the Lord.
2. We are the people of the Lord.
3. These are the praises of the Lord.

SECTION 2

KNEEL AND ADORE

SONGS OF WORSHIP

15. Turn me, O God

Quietly and slowly
Refrain
Jodi Page
D
Turn me, O God, and
A7
D
1.
Fine
2.
I shall be turned.
G
A
D
1. Though I wander through des - - - o - la-tion,
OMIT
2. Cre - ate in me a new heart.
3. You have led us out of bon - dage,
verse 1 only

G
A
D
I will find you there.
I would see your face.
you have kept us well.
G
A
D
Though the wa-ters o'er - whelm my soul,
Take not your ho - ly Spi - rit from me,
Ev - en in the face of our com-plaint,
A7
D
D.C.
ev - en so you are Lord.
D.C.
OMIT
I would see your face.
you have loved us still.
verse 1 only
D.C.

16. Jesus, I love you

Kathleen Thomerson

Simply and softly, not too slow
love, love you.
Je - sus, I love you, Je - sus, I love you,
Je - sus, I love you, take my life.
1. Life is your
2. Now I have
3. Love reach-es
gift, I give my heart, kneel and a - dore you, and I
seen the love of God. He has poured out the Spi-rit of
out both near and far, and so we fol-low where you
1-2.
3.
know that
truth. lead us.
Je - sus, I fol-low, Je - sus, I
Je - sus, I love you, Je - sus, I

fol-low, Je - sus, I fol-low, all my life.
love you. Je - sus, I love you, take my life.

17. Jesus, Jesus

May be sung as a 2, 3, or 4-part round.

Anon.
Arr. Betty Pulkingham

Slowly, fervently

1 Em D Em Bm7 2 Em D
Je - sus, Je - sus, let me tell you

Em Bm7 3 Em D Em Bm7
what I — know. You have giv - en us your spi - rit;

4 Em D Em Bm7 E *final ending*
we love you so. so.

18. The Shepherd of my soul

Kathleen Thomerson

Tenderly
1. I sing to the shep-herd of my soul all the day as he leads me through this world. To fol-low him, to tru-ly fol-low in his way is to live a life of love.
2. I sing to the shep-herd of my soul all the night for the path is clear to him. And when I sleep, he makes a shel-ter of his light; when I wake he leads me on.
3. All my life, O shep-herd of my soul, I will sing with a heart that's full of joy. To fol-low you is just to trust that you will bring all your sheep in-to the fold.
Refrain
All I am I of-fer Je-sus, sing-ing praises un-to him.

Oh, my soul, give thanks to Je - sus, for he is your shep-herd - king.

19. Come into his presence

Anon.

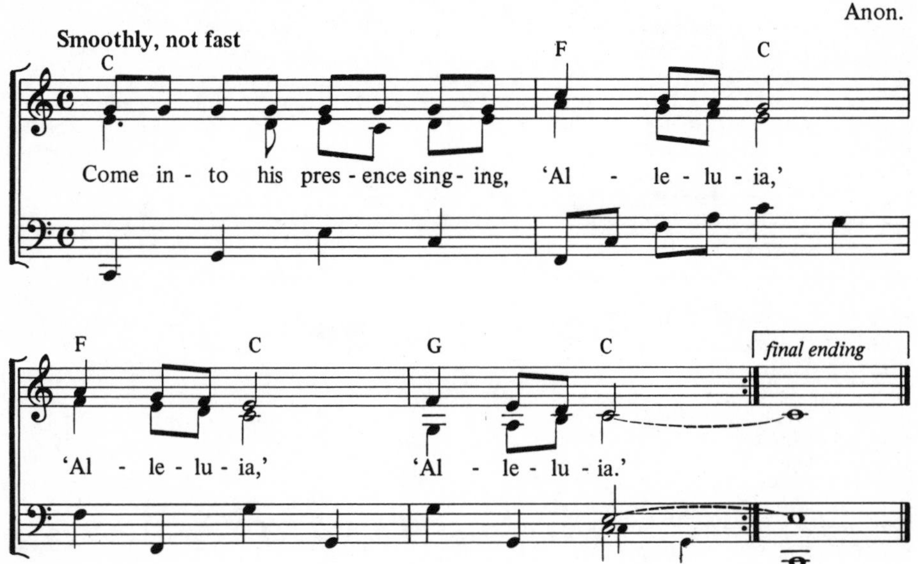

Smoothly, not fast
C
F
C
Come in - to his pres - ence sing - ing, 'Al - le - lu - ia,'
F
C
G
C
final ending
'Al - le - lu - ia,' 'Al - le - lu - ia.'

Other verses may be added:

Come into his presence singing,
'Jesus is Lord'..........
'Worthy the Lamb'.......
'Glory to God'.......

20. My song is love unknown

Samuel Crossman

John Ireland

Fervently, not slow

1. My song is love un - known, My Sa-viour's love to
2. He came from his blest throne Sal - va - tion to be-
3. Some-times they strew his way And his sweet prais - es
me; Love to the love - less shown, That they might
stow; But men made strange, and none The longed - for
sing; Re - sound - ing all the day Ho - san - nas
love - - - - ly be. O who am I, that
Christ would know: But O, my friend, my
to their King. Then 'Cru - ci - fy!' is
for my sake My Lord should take frail flesh and die?
friend in - deed, Who at my need his life did spend.
all their breath, And for his death they thirst and cry.

4. They rise and needs will have
My dear Lord made away;
A murderer they save,
The Prince of life they slay,
Yet cheerful he to suff'ring goes,
That he his foes from thence might free.

5. In life, no house, no home
My Lord on earth might have;
In death, no friendly tomb,
But what a stranger gave.
What may I say? Heaven was his home;
But mine the tomb wherein he lay.

6. Here might I stay and sing,
No story so divine;
Never was love, dear King,
Never was grief like thine.
This is my friend, in whose sweet praise
I all my days could gladly spend.

21. I love the name of Jesus

Capo 3 (D) Kathleen Thomerson

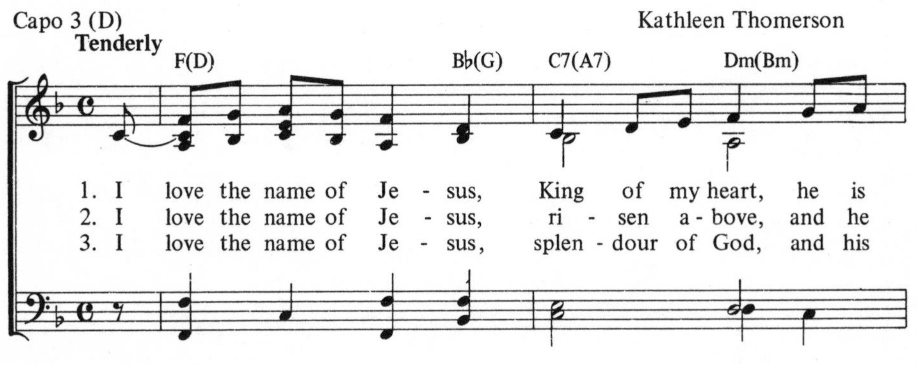
Tenderly
F(D)
Bb(G)
C7(A7)
Dm(Bm)
1. I love the name of Je - sus, King of my heart, he is
2. I love the name of Je - sus, ri - sen a - bove, and he
3. I love the name of Je - sus, splen - dour of God, and his

Gm(Em)
C7(A7)
F(D)
Bb(G)
ev' - ry - thing to me. I bless the name of Je - sus,
loves and prays for me. I bless the name of Je - sus,
face I long to see. I bless the name of Je - sus,

C7(A7) Dm(Bm) Gm(Em) C7(A7) F(D) F7(D7)
reign in my life, show the Fa - ther's love so free.
rul - ing on high with a glo - rious ma - jes - ty.
shep - herd of men; by his side I now can be.
Bb(G) F(D)
Spi - rit of love, spi - rit of power,
Gm(Em) G7(E7) C(A) C7(A7) F(D) Bb(G)
shine through e - ter - ni - ty.
I love the name of Je - sus,
I praise the name of Je - sus,
I praise the name of Je - sus,
C7(A7) Dm(Bm) Gm(Em) C7(A7) F(D)
light of the world, let me walk each day with thee.
Lord of my life, for he died to set me free.
for he is love, and that love he gives to me.

22. Blessed be the name

Capo 1 (E)

Anon.
Arr. Betty Pulkingham

Gently
F(E)
F7(E7)
Bb(A)
F(E)
1. Bless - ed be the name, bless - ed be the name,
C7(B7)
Bless - ed be the name of the Lord.
F(E)
F7(E7)
Bb(A)
F(E)
Bless - ed be the name, bless - ed be the name,
Bb(A)
F/C(E/B)
C7(B7)
F(E)
Bb(A)
F(E)
Bless - ed be the name of the Lord.

2. Jesus is the name, Jesus is the name,
Jesus is the name of the Lord. } *repeat*

3. Worthy to be praised, worthy to be praised,
Worthy to be praised is the Lord. } *repeat*

23. Glory

Capo 3 (D)
Mimi Farra
Freely
F(D)
F Maj7 (D Maj7)
F +6 (D +6)
C7 (A7)
1. Sing to the Lord, sing to the Lord of Lords.
Flowing
Gm7 (Em7)
C7 (A7)
Glo - - - - - - - - ry, glo - - - - - - - - ry,
Gm7 (Em7)
C7 (A7)
glo - - - - - - - - ry, glo - - - - - - - ry,
F(D) C7 (A7) F(D)
1.
F(D) C7 (A7) F(D)
2.
1. 2. 3. glo - ry to the Lord. Son. Lamb. glo - ry to the Lord. Son. Lamb.
4. glo - ry Je - sus Christ. glo - ry Je - sus Christ.

F(D)
F Maj7 (D Maj7)
2, 3. Sing, oh sing to the Son / Lamb of God,
4. Sing, oh sing to the Word of God, the
F +6(D +6)
C7 (A7)
D.S.
Sing, for he is wor - - - thy of
D.S.*
Word made flesh in Je - sus Christ.
D.S.
Descant (for soprano solo or a few treble voices)
Glo - - - - - ry, glo - - - - - ry, glo - - - - - - - - - - - - - ry, glo - ry Je - sus Christ. Glo - - - - - - - - - - - - ry, glo - ry, glo - - - - - - - - - ry, glo - ry Je - sus Christ.

* Following verse 4 the refrain may be repeated several times, beginning softly, increasing volume and momentum as repetitions occur, and adding the following descant on the final refrain:

24. Sweet Jesus

Anon.
Arr. Life and Soul Group

Easy rock beat
E
A
E
G♯
C♯m
Sweet Je - - - - - - - - -
A
E
G♯
C♯m
A
sus, sweet Je - - - - - - - - - sus,
E
E7
li - ly of the val-ley, bright as the morning

A
G♯m
F♯m
star. Sweet Je - - - - - - - - - sus, sweet
E
G♯
C♯m
A
E
Je - - - - - - - - - sus, he's the God of ev' - ry
B7
A
E
na-tion, bless his name.

2. How I love him, how I love him,
 Lily of the valley, bright as the morning star.
How I love him, how I love him,
 He's the God of every nation,
  Bless his name.

3. Jesus loves you.....
4. Sweet Jesus.....

25. Sweet Jesus

Paul Goodwin
Arr. Betty Pulkingham

Simply

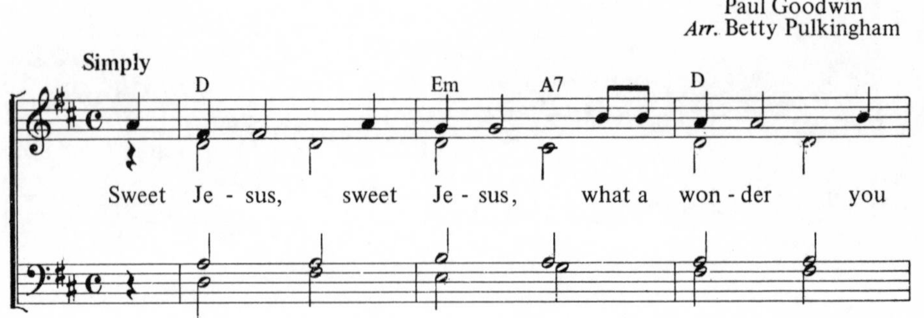
D
Em
A7
D
Sweet Je - sus, sweet Je - sus, what a won - der you

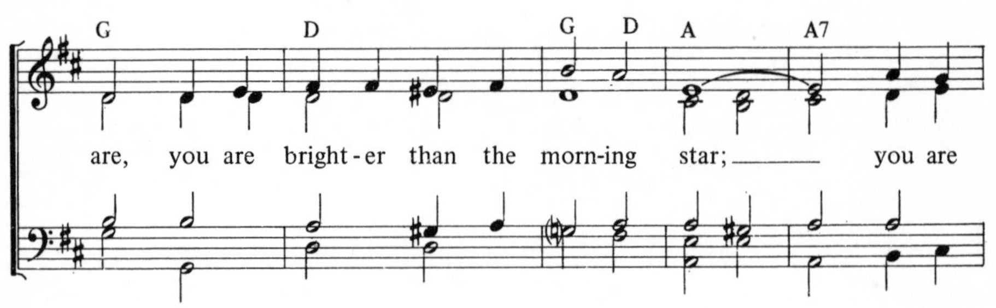
G
D
G D
A
A7
are, you are bright - er than the morn-ing star; you are

D
Em
A7
D
D7
fair - er, much fair - er than the li - ly that grows by the

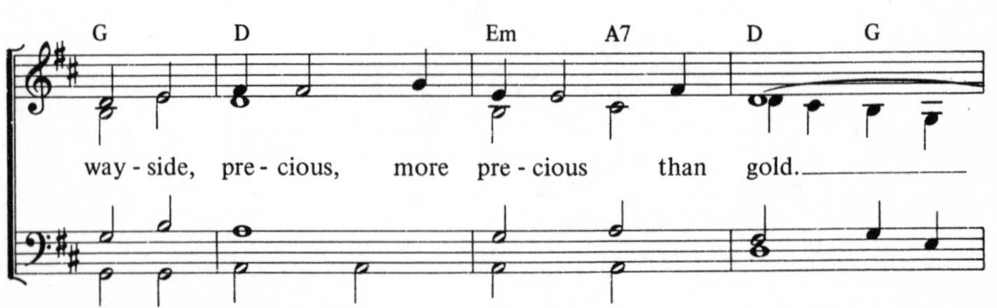
G
D
Em
A7
D
G
way - side, pre - cious, more pre - cious than gold.

D
D7
G
D
You are the rose of Sha-ron, the fair-est of the

A7
D
G
D
A
fair, you are all my heart could e'er de - sire.

A7
D
Em
A7
D
D7
Sweet Je-sus, sweet Je-sus, what a won-der you

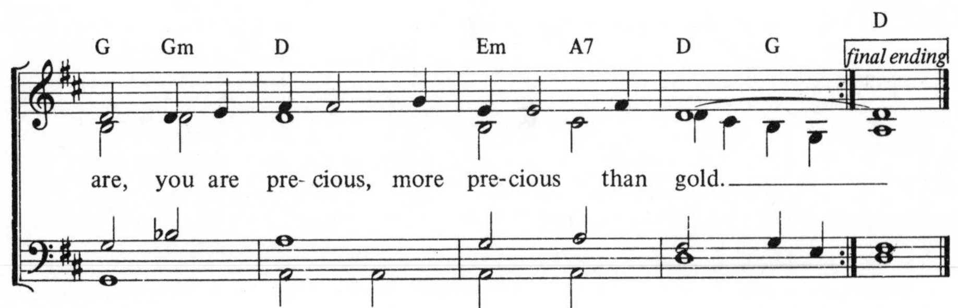
G
Gm
D
Em
A7
D
G
D
final ending
are, you are pre-cious, more pre-cious than gold.

26. God gives peace like a river

Anon.
Arr. Betty Pulkingham

Steadily
E
E7
A
God gives peace like a riv - er, peace like a
B7(E*)
E
F♯
B7
riv - er, God gives peace like a riv - er in my soul.
E
E7
A
God gives peace like a riv - er, peace like a
B7(E*)
C♯m(E*)
F♯m(E/B*) B7
E
A
E
riv - er, God gives peace like a riv - er in my soul.

Other verses may be added:
God gives love ..... joy ..... faith ..... hope ..... praise ... *etc.*

*Use these chords if guitar plays alone.

27. O worship the Lord in the beauty of holiness

John S.B. Monsell

'Was lebet, was schwebet'

With breadth and feeling
1. O worship the Lord in the beau-ty of ho-li-ness, Bow down be-fore him, his glo-ry pro-claim; With gold of o-be-dience and in-cense of low-li-ness, Kneel and a-dore him, the Lord is his name.
2. Low at his feet lay thy bur-den of care-ful-ness, High on his heart he will bear it for thee, Com-fort thy sor-rows and an-swer thy prayer-ful-ness, Guid-ing thy steps as may best for thee be.
3. Fear not to en-ter his courts in the slen-der-ness, Of the poor wealth thou would'st reck-on as thine; Truth in its beau-ty, and love in its ten-der-ness, These are the off'rings to lay on his shrine.

4. These, though we bring them in trembling and fearfulness,
 He will accept for the name that is dear;
Mornings of joy give for evenings of tearfulness,
 Trust for our trembling, and hope for our fear.

5. O worship the Lord . . . . *(same as verse 1)*

28. My Jesus, I love thee

Capo 1 (E)
W. R. Featherston
A. J. Gordon
Soft and intense
(E)* (A) (E) (B7) (E)
1. My Jesus, I love thee, I know thou art mine, For
2. I love thee because thou hast first loved me, And
3. I'll love thee in life, I will love thee in death, And
(A) (E) (B7) (E)
thee all the follies of sin I resign. My
purchased my pardon on Calvary's tree. I
praise thee as long as thou lendest me breath; And
(A) (E) (C♯m) (B7) (E) (A) (E) (B7)
gracious Redeemer, my Saviour art thou:
love thee for wearing the thorns on thy brow:
say when the death-dew lies cold on my brow:
If
(E) (A) (E) (C♯m) (B7) (E)
ever I loved thee, my Jesus, 'tis now.

* Guitar chords and 4-part harmonization not designed to be used together.

4. In mansions of glory and endless delight,
I'll ever adore thee in heaven so bright;
I'll sing with the glittering crown on my brow;
If ever I loved thee, my Jesus, 'tis now.

29. Turn your eyes upon Jesus

Capo 1 (E)

H. H. Lemmel

Reverently

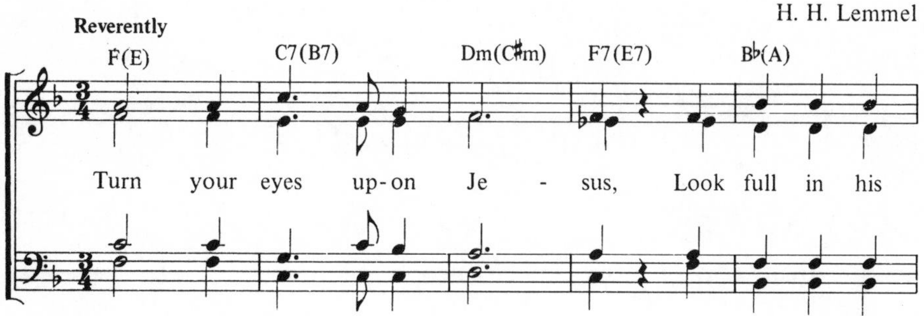
F(E) C7(B7) Dm(C♯m) F7(E7) B♭(A)
Turn your eyes up-on Je - sus, Look full in his

C7(B7) F(E) F7(E7)
won-der - ful face; And the things of earth will grow

Dm(C♯m) B♭(A) F(E) C7(B7) F(E)
strange- ly dim In the light of his glo - ry and grace.

30. Jesus, the very thought of thee

Tr. Edward Caswall

'Windsor'
M. William Damon
Descant by Betty Pulkingham

With awe; not slow
3. O hope of ev' - ry con - trite heart, O joy of all the meek, To those who fall, how kind thou art, how good to those, to those who seek!
5. Je - sus, our on - ly joy be thou, as thou our prize will be, In thee be all our glo - ry now and thro' e - ter - ni - ty.
1. Je - sus, the ve - ry thought of thee With sweet-ness fills the breast; But sweet- er far thy face to see, And in thy pre - sence rest.
2. No voice can sing, no heart can frame, Nor can the mem - ory find, A sweet- er sound than Je - sus' name, The Sa - viour of man - kind.
3. O hope of ev' - ry con - trite heart, O joy of all the meek, To those who fall, how kind thou art! How good to those who seek!

4. But what to those who find? Ah, this
   Nor tongue nor pen can show;
   The love of Jesus, what it is,
   None but who love him know.

5. Jesus, our only joy be thou,
   As thou our prize wilt be;
   In thee be all our glory now,
   And through eternity.

31. My God, how wonderful thou art

Frederick William Faber

'Windsor'
M. William Damon

1. My God, how wonderful thou art,
   Thy majesty how bright!
   How beautiful thy mercy-seat,
   In depths of burning light!

2. How dread are thine eternal years,
   O everlasting Lord,
   By prostrate spirits day and night
   Incessantly adored!

3. O how I fear thee, living God,
   With deepest tenderest fears,
   And worship thee with trembling hope,
   And penitential tears.

4. Yet I may love thee too, O Lord,
   Almighty as thou art,
   For thou hast stooped to ask of me
   The love of my poor heart.

5. How wonderful, how beautiful,
   The sight of thee must be,
   Thine endless wisdom, boundless power,
   And aweful purity.

SECTION 3

LITURGICAL SONGS

INTROIT

32. Come and dine

C. B. Widmeyer
Arr. Betty Pulkingham

Cheerfully
A
D
Bm
1. Je - sus has a ta - ble spread where the saints of God are fed, he in-
2. The dis - ci - ples came to land, thus o - bey - ing Christ's com-mand, for the
3. Soon the Lamb will take his bride to be ev - er at his side, all the
E7
A
vites his cho - sen peo - ple, 'Come and dine.' With his
mas - ter called to them, 'Oh come and dine.' There they
host of hea - ven will as - sem - bled be. Oh, 'twill
D
Bm
man - na he doth feed and sup - plies our ev' - ry need, oh, 'tis
found their heart's de - sire, bread and fish up - on the fire. Thus he
be a glo - rious sight, all the saints in spot - less white, and with

E7
A
Refrain
sweet to sup with Je - sus all the time!
sat - is - fies the hun - gry ev' - ry time. 'Come and
Je - sus they will feast e - ter - nal - ly.
E7
A
dine,' the mas - ter call - eth. 'Come and dine.' You may
D
B7
E
feast at Je - sus' ta - ble all the time. He who
A
D
Bm
fed the mul - ti - tude, turned the wa - ter in - to wine, to the
E7
A
hun - gry call - eth now, 'Come and dine.'

33. I will arise

Capo 3 (A) Mimi Farra

With pulsing rhythm
C(A)
Bb(G)
C(A)
I will a - rise so ear - ly in the morn - ing, rise to

Gm(Em)
C(A)
sing my Sa - viour's prais - es; rise with

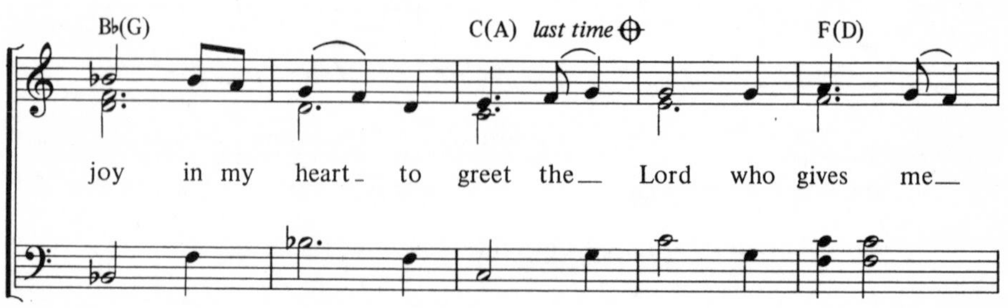
Bb(G)
C(A) last time
F(D)
joy in my heart to greet the Lord who gives me

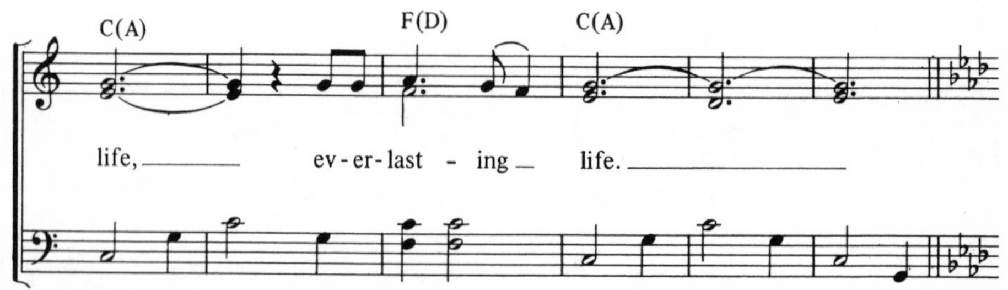
C(A)
F(D)
C(A)
life, ev - er - last - ing life.

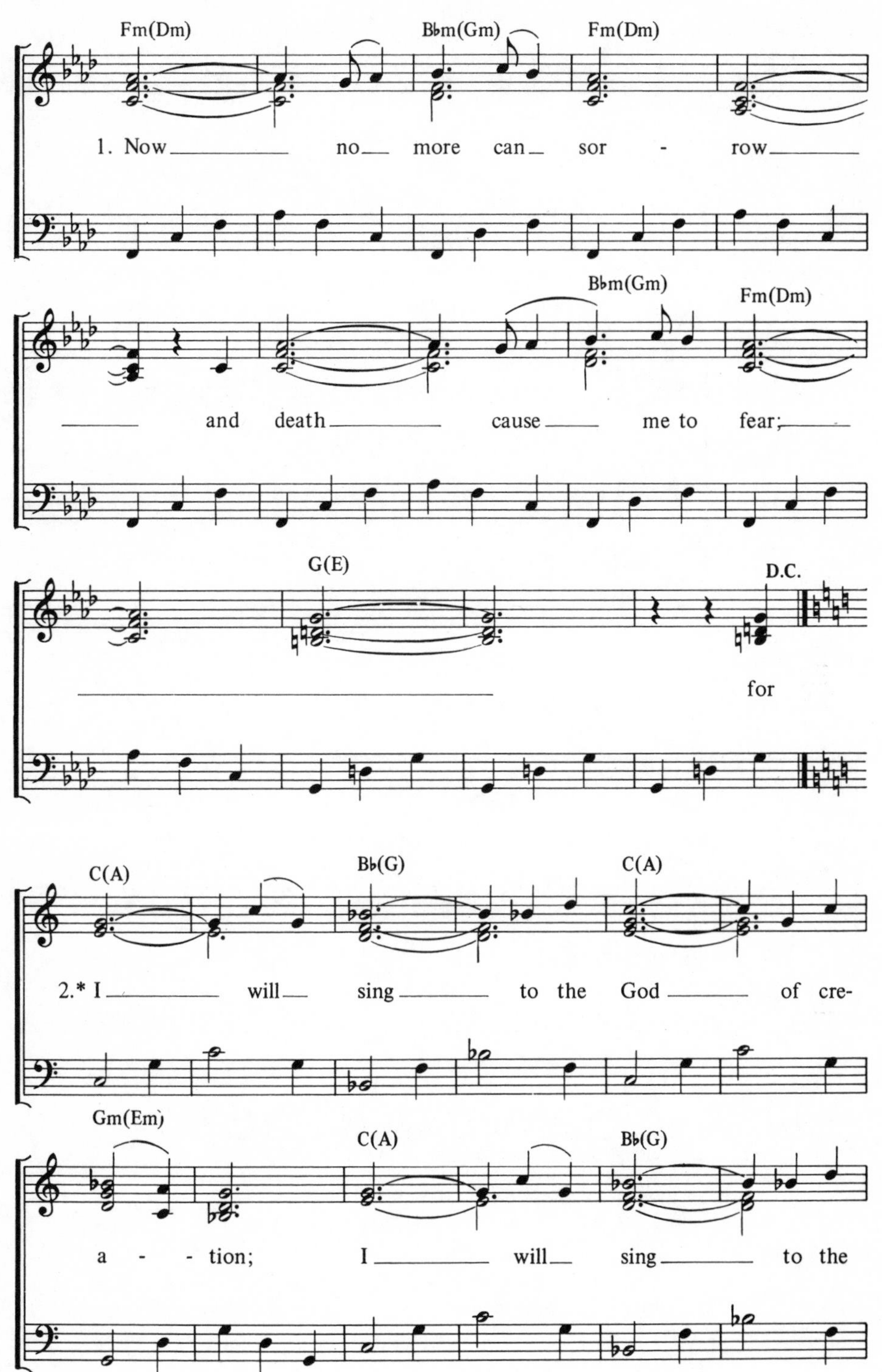
Fm(Dm)
Bbm(Gm)
Fm(Dm)
1. Now no more can sor - row
Bbm(Gm)
Fm(Dm)
and death cause me to fear;
G(E)
D.C.
for
C(A)
Bb(G)
C(A)
2.* I will sing to the God of cre-
Gm(Em)
C(A)
Bb(G)
a - - tion; I will sing to the

C(A) last time
Gm(Em)
C(A)
D.C.
Lord of love.

last time
F(D)
C(A)
of love, ev-er
Lord who gives me life, ev-er

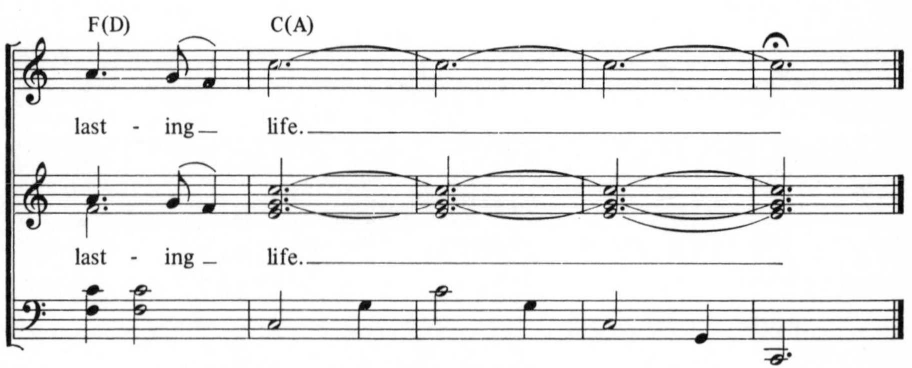
F(D)
C(A)
last - ing life.
last - ing life.

* Verse 2 is a musical complement to the refrain, and the two may be sung together as a final (additional) refrain, using the ending marked *'last time.'*

34. Allelu

Mimi Farra
With a lilt
E
A
E
B7
1. Come and bless, come and praise, come and praise the liv - ing God.
Refrain: Al - le - lu, al - le - lu, al - le - lu - ia, Je - sus Christ.
Al - le - lu, al - le - lu, al - le - lu - ia, Je - sus
Christ.
final ending

2. Come and seek, come and find, come and find the living God.
   Allelu, allelu, alleluia, Jesus Christ. *Refrain.*

3. Come and hear, come and know, come and know the living God.
   Allelu, allelu, alleluia, Jesus Christ. *Refrain.*

4. Come and bless, come and praise, come and praise the Word of God;
   Word of God, Word made flesh, alleluia, Jesus Christ. *Refrain.*

Seasonal verses:

5. Come behold, come and see, come and see the new-born babe.
   Allelu, allelu, alleluia, Jesus Christ. *Refrain.*

6. Angel choirs sing above, 'Glory to the Son of God!'
   Shepherd folk sing below, 'Allelu, Emmanuel!' *Refrain.*

35. I trust in thee, O Lord

(Psalm 31)

M. Mc Allister
Arr. Jeanne Harper

Smoothly
D
C
D
I trust in thee, O Lord.
F♯m
Bm
Em
I say, 'Thou art my God.'
A7
Bm
F♯m
Em
A7
My times are in thy hand.
D
Em7
A7
D
my times are in thy hand.

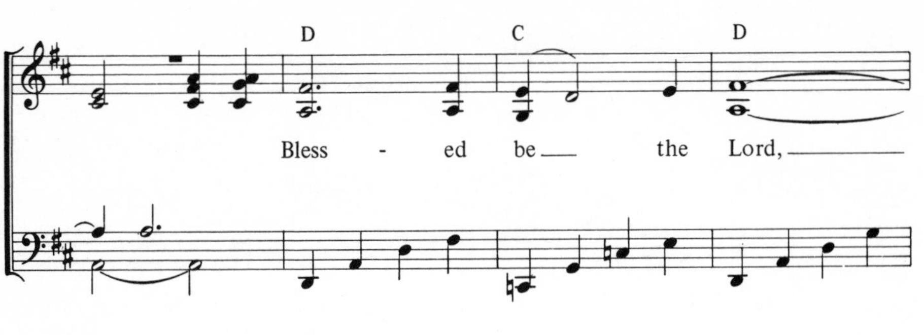
D
C
D
Bless - ed be the Lord,

F♯m
Bm
Em7
for he has won-drous - ly shown

A7
Bm7
F♯m
Em
A7
his stead - fast love to me,

D
Em7
A7
D
his stead - fast love to me.

36. O magnify the Lord

(Based on Psalm 34)

Capo 5 (Am)

Ruth Wieting

With an easy rhythmic swing
Dm(Am)
Am7(Em7)
O mag - ni - fy the Lord with
Dm(Am)
Am7(Em7)
me, let us praise
Am7 Dm Am7
Dm(Am)
1. (Em7) (Am) (Em7)
his name to - geth - er. O
2. Fine
Gm(Dm)
1. I will bless the Lord at
2. I cried un to the
3. O trust the Lord, you
4. O come, you sons of

Dm(Am) Gm(Dm) Dm(Am)

all times, his praise will al - ways
Lord, and he has freed me
saints, for those who trust him
God, to be the bo - dy

Am7(Em7) Dm(Am) Am7 (Em7) Dm (Am) Am7 (Em7) D.C.

be in my mouth.
from all my fears.
lack no good thing.
of Je - sus Christ.

O

D.C.

37. There is a river

(Psalm 46)

Psalm 46: 4-5

Jonathan Asprey

Fast, rollicking tempo *(1 beat to a bar)*

G
There is a riv - er whose

C
Em
Am
streams make glad the ci - ty of
G
last time
God, the ci - ty of
Dsus4
D
God; the
G
C
ho - ly hab - i - ta - tion of
Em
Am
G
the most high, the ci - ty of God,

D
G
C
G
Fine
the ci-ty of God.
C
God is in the midst of her,
G
Em
she shall not be moved;
A
A7
the Lord of hosts is
D
D.C.
with her.
For

38. O give thanks unto the Lord

(Psalm 136)

Kathleen Thomerson

Joyfully
Refrain
G
C
O give thanks un-to the Lord, for he is good,
D7
G
for his mer - cy en - dur - eth for - ev - er.

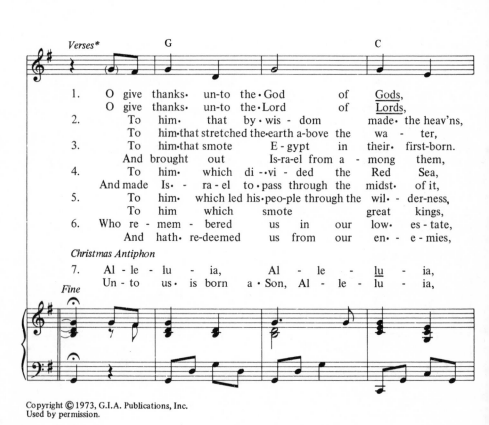

*Verses**

G C

1. O give thanks· un-to the·God of Gods,
O give thanks· un-to the·Lord of Lords,
2. To him· that by·wis - dom made· the heav'ns,
To him·that stretched the·earth a-bove the wa - ter,
3. To him·that smote E - gypt in their· first-born.
And brought out Is-ra-el from a - mong them,
4. To him· which di -·vi - ded the Red Sea,
And made Is· - ra - el to·pass through the midst· of it,
5. To him· which led his·peo-ple through the wil· - der-ness,
To him which smote great kings,
6. Who re - mem - bered us in our low· es - tate,
And hath· re-deemed us from our en· - e - mies,

Christmas Antiphon

7. Al - le - lu - ia, Al - le - lu - ia,
Un - to us· is born a·Son, Al - le - lu - ia,

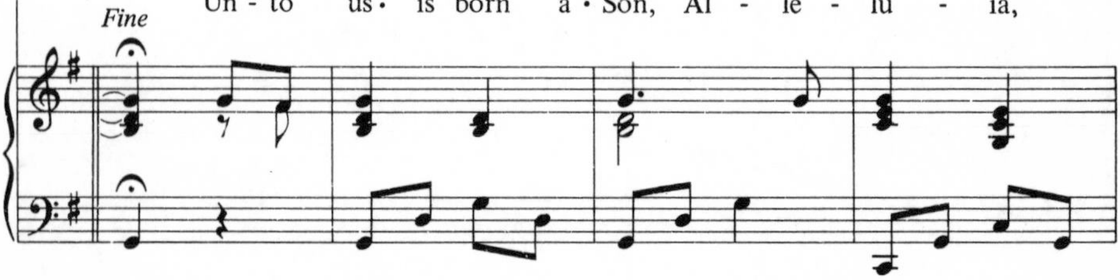

Fine

D
G
For his mer - cy en - dur - eth for - ev - er.
D
G
1. To him who a - lone do - eth great won-
2. To him that made great
3. With a strong hand and with a stretched out
4. But ov - er - threw Pha - roah and all his
5. And gave them land for an her - i -
6. O give thanks un - to the God of hea - - -
7. And he shall rule with e - qui -
D
G
3
Refrain
ders,
lights,
arm,
host,
tage,
ven,
ty,
For his mer - cy en - dur - eth for - ev - er.
3
D.C.

*1. Underlined syllables are sung on more than one melody note.
2. A dot (•) shows where to change melody note.

39. The song of Simeon

(Nunc Dimittis)

Capo 3 (E)

Luke 2: 29-32

Mimi Farra

Gently
G(E)
G sus4 (E sus4)
Lord, you have ful - filled your word;
G(E)
F(D)
now let your ser - vant de - part in
G sus4 (E sus4)
(G sus4(E sus4) G (E)
G(E)
1.
2.
fine
peace.
C(A)
G(E)
1. With my own eyes I have seen the sal - va - tion, which
2. A light to re - veal you (𝄽) to the na - tions, and the

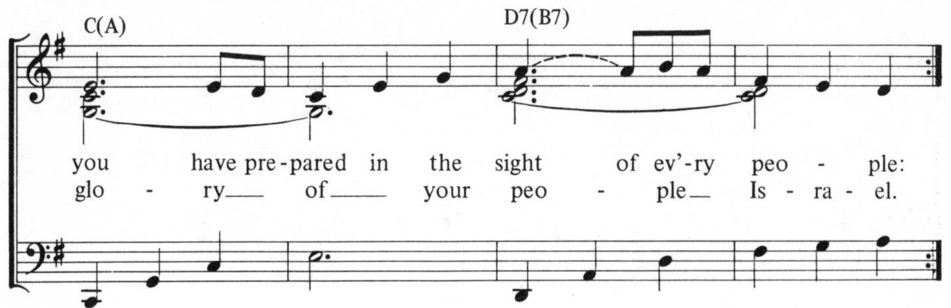
C(A)
D7(B7)
you have pre-pared in the sight of ev'-ry peo - ple:
glo - ry___ of___ your peo - ple___ Is - ra - el.

40. My soul doth magnify the Lord

(Magnificat)

Luke 1: 46-47, 49.

Composer and author unknown
Arr. Betty Pulkingham

Gently

D A7 D

My soul doth mag-ni-fy___ the Lord, and my

A7

spi - rit hath re-joiced in God my sa - viour for___

D D7 G D A7

he that is might-y hath done great things, and ho - ly is his

D
A
name. My soul doth mag - ni - fy the Lord, my soul doth
D
E
E7
mag - ni - fy the Lord, and my spi - rit hath re - joiced in God my
A
D
D7
sa - viour for he that is might - y hath done
G
D
A7
great things, and ho - ly is his
D
1.
D
2.
name. My soul doth name.

41. Jesus, Lamb of God

(Agnus Dei)

From *'Mass for the King of Glory'* Betty Pulkingham

Slow and sustained
D
Bm
Em
A
G
1.
2.
Je - sus, Lamb of God, have mer - cy on us. Je - sus, bear-er of our sins, have mer - cy on us. Je - sus, re-deem-er of the world, give us your peace. Give us your peace.

The publishers are grateful to the International Consultation on English Texts for the use of their copyright material.

42. Calypso Doxology

Thomas Ken
Verse 2 - Deanna Wheeler

'Jamaica Farewell'
Lord Burgess
Arr. Betty Pulkingham

With an easy swing
A
D
1. Praise God from whom all bless-ings flow, praise him
2. Hal - le - lu - jah! Got the vic - to - ry
3. A - men, a - men, a - men, a - men, a - men,
A
E7
A
all ye crea - tures here be - low.
o - ver Sa - tan and o - ver sin.
a - men, a - men, a - men, a - men.
A
D
Praise him a - bove, ye heav'n - ly host, praise him
(7) Je - sus Christ is a - live to - day and he
A - men, a - men, a - men, a - men, a - men,

A
E7
A
final ending
Fa - ther, Son and Ho - ly Ghost.
leads and guides me all the way.
a - men, a - men, a - men, a - men.

43. Tallis' Canon

Thomas Tallis
'Evening Hymn'

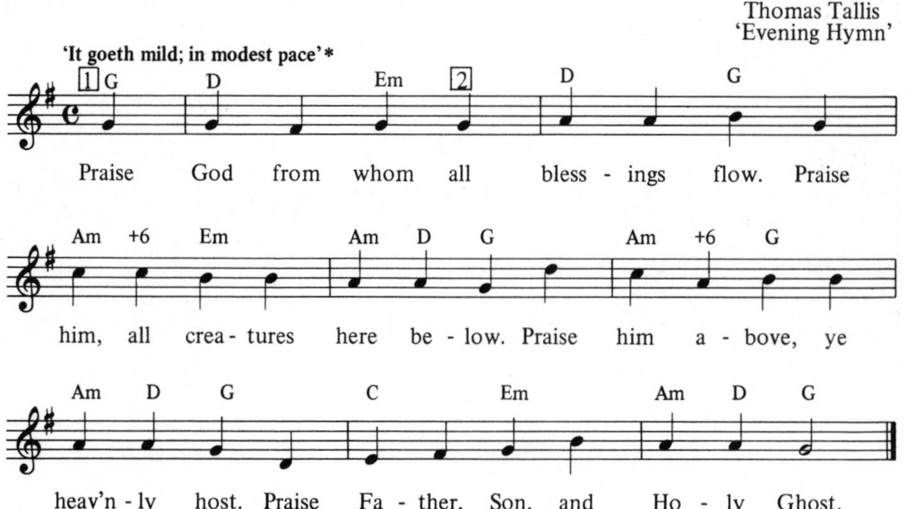
'It goeth mild; in modest pace'*
1 G D Em 2 D G
Praise God from whom all bless - ings flow. Praise
Am +6 Em Am D G Am +6 G
him, all crea - tures here be - low. Praise him a - bove, ye
Am D G C Em Am D G
heav'n - ly host. Praise Fa - ther, Son, and Ho - ly Ghost.

Archbishop Parker's Psalter, c. 1567

44. Doxology

Thomas Ken Jimmy Owens

With movement
E
G♯m
A
Praise God from whom all bless - ings
E
A
E
B7
flow; Praise him all crea - tures here be-
E
G♯m
A
low. Praise him a - bove ye hea - ven-ly
E
A
E
B7
E
hosts; Praise Fa - ther, Son, and Ho - ly Ghost.

Optional 4-part setting

† E G♯m A E
Praise God from whom all bless - ings flow; Praise
A E B7 E ✻
him all crea - tures here be - low. Praise
G♯m A E
him a - bove ye hea - ven- ly host; Praise
Praise him
A E B7 E E
1, 2. final ending
Fa - ther, Son, and Ho - ly Ghost. Praise Ghost.

† One very attractive way to sing this song in parts:

First time:	Sopranos begin	Add altos at mid-point*
Second time:	Tenors join	Basses too (at mid-point)*
Third time:	All sing	

45. The Lord's Prayer

Jodi Page

Slow and sustained
D
D Maj7
Am7
Our Fa - ther in hea-ven, hal-lowed be your
G
A
name. Your king-dom come, your will be done on
G
D
earth as in hea-ven.
D Maj7
Am7
Give us to-day our dai-ly bread. For-give us our
G
A
G
sins as we for-give those who sin a-

D
cresc. . . . .
gainst us.
Do not bring us to the
D Maj7
Am7
time of trial
but de-liv - er us from
8
G
D
D Maj7
e - vil.
For the king - dom, the pow - er, and the
Am7
G
glo - ry are yours now and for-
A
A7
slowly
D
ev - er.
A - - men.

46. Hallowed be thy name

Traditional
Arr. Betty Pulkingham

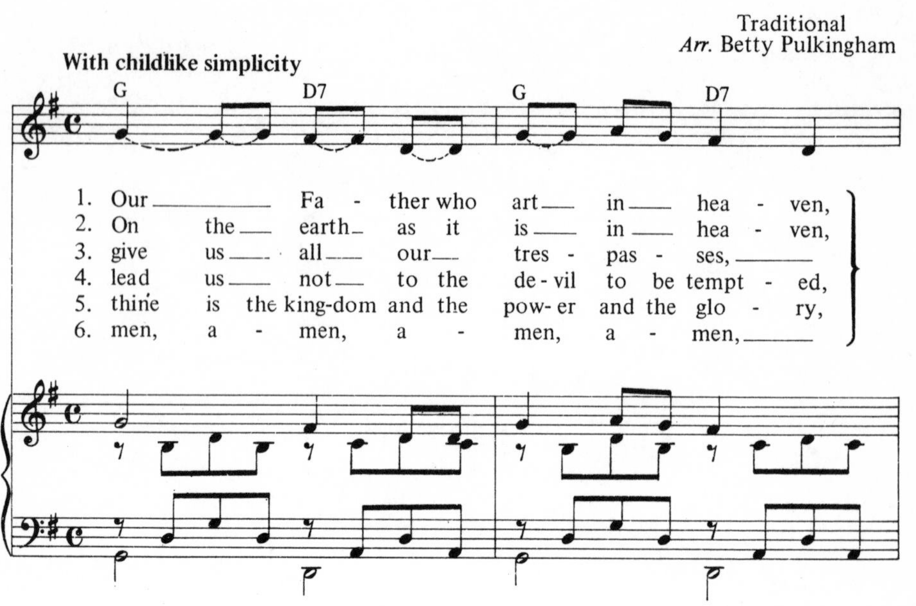
With childlike simplicity
G
D7
G
D7
1. Our Fa - ther who art in hea - ven,
2. On the earth as it is in hea - ven,
3. give us all our tres - pas - ses,
4. lead us not to the de - vil to be tempt - ed,
5. thine is the king-dom and the pow- er and the glo - ry,
6. men, a - men, a - men, a - men,

G
D7
G
Hal - low - ed be thy name.
Thy
Give
As
But de-
For -
A-

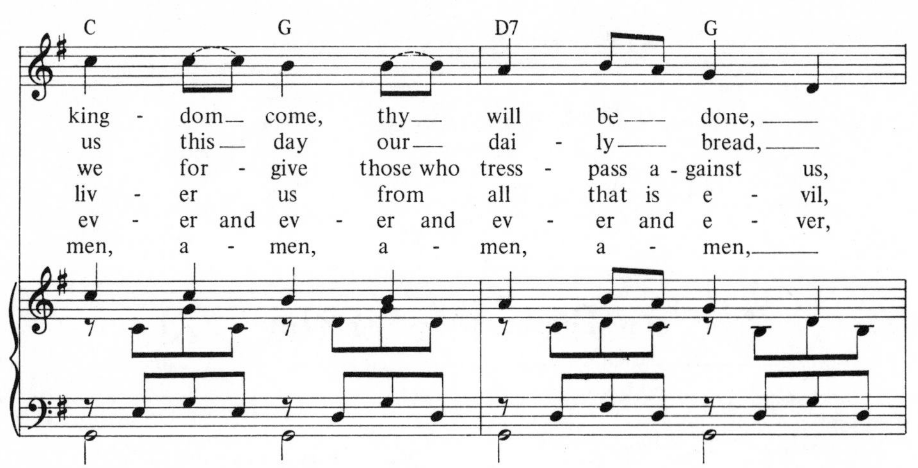
C
G
D7
G
king - dom— come, thy— will be— done,—
us this— day our— dai - ly— bread,—
we for - give those who tress - pass a - gainst us,
liv - er us from all that is e - vil,
ev - er and ev - er and ev - er and e - ver,
men, a - men, a - men, a - men,—

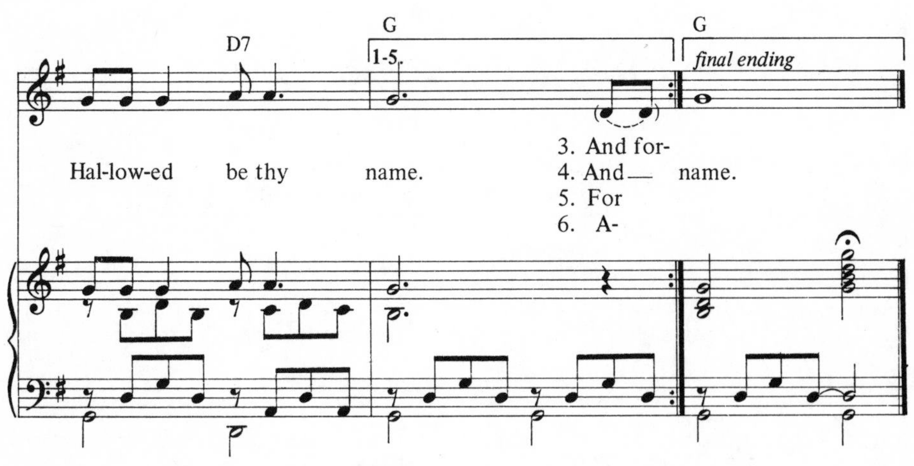
D7
G
G
1-5.
final ending
Hal-low-ed be thy name.
3. And for-
4. And— name.
5. For
6. A-

SECTION 4

BECOME....

SONGS OF WHOLENESS AND MATURITY

47. The steadfast love of the Lord

Capo 4 (C)

Edith Mc Neill

With a rocking rhythm
Refrain E(C)*
A(F)
E(C)
The stead-fast love of the Lord nev-er ceas - es; his mer-cies
A(F)
B(G)
A(F)
F#m(Dm)
nev - er come to an end. They are new ev'- ry morn-ing,
G#m(Em)
C#m(Am)
F#m(Dm7)
B(G)
E(C) B(G) E(C)
new ev'- ry morn-ing. Great is thy faith - ful - ness, O Lord!
A(F)
B(G)
E(C)
Vss. 2-4
Fine
A(F)
Great is thy faith-ful - ness. 1. The Lord is my por-tion, says my

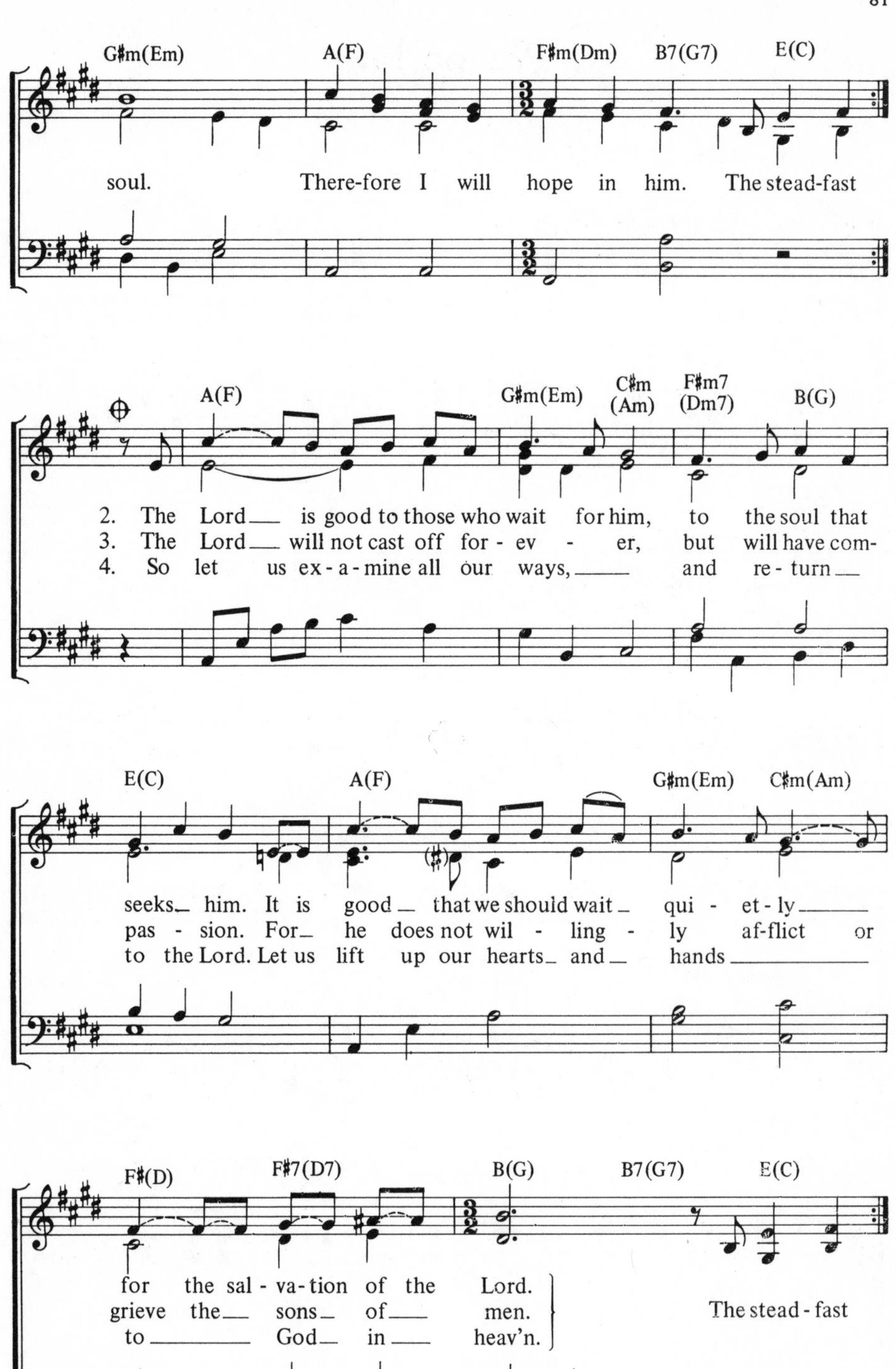
G♯m(Em) A(F) F♯m(Dm) B7(G7) E(C)
soul. There-fore I will hope in him. The stead-fast
A(F) G♯m(Em) C♯m (Am) F♯m7 (Dm7) B(G)
2. The Lord __ is good to those who wait for him, to the soul that
3. The Lord __ will not cast off for - ev - er, but will have com-
4. So let us ex - a - mine all our ways, __ and re - turn __
E(C) A(F) G♯m(Em) C♯m(Am)
seeks __ him. It is good __ that we should wait __ qui - et - ly __
pas - sion. For __ he does not wil - ling - ly af-flict or
to the Lord. Let us lift up our hearts __ and __ hands __
F♯(D) F♯7(D7) B(G) B7(G7) E(C)
for the sal - va - tion of the Lord.
grieve the __ sons __ of __ men.
to __ God __ in __ heav'n.
The stead - fast

*Guitar chords and piano arrangement not designed to be used together.

48. Put on love

Col. 3: 12-16

Jodi Page

Folk-rock

Refrain
E
A
Put
on
E
1.
love,
E
2.
love.
And the
A
B7
E
peace of God
that binds us
all
to-geth - er

A
will keep our hearts in

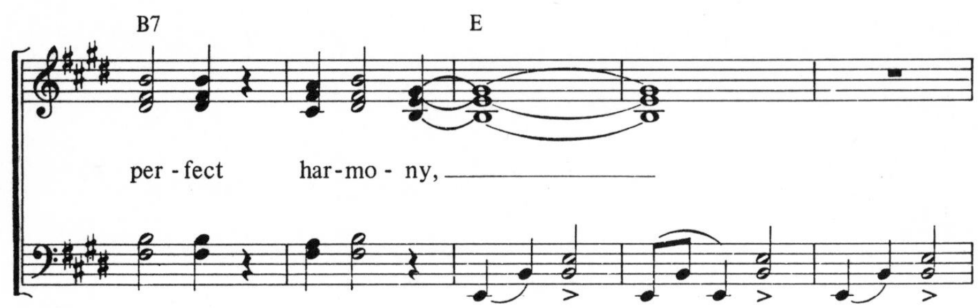
B7
E
per - fect har-mo - ny,

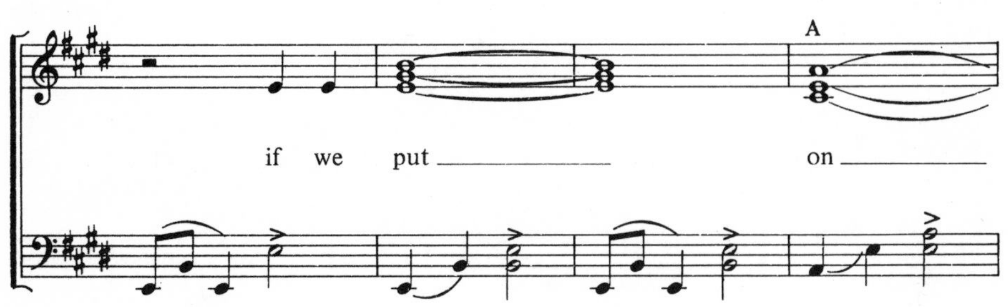
A
if we put
on

E
last time
love.

A
1. We are God's cho - sen race, his
2. God has for - giv - en us, now
3. Al - ways be thank - ful and
B7
E
saints, and he loves us.
we should for - give our bro - ther.
let the mes - sage of Je - - sus
A
We should be clothed in peace, in
We should show gen - tle - ness and
in all its rich-ness find a

B7
E
D.C.
kind - ness, and hu - mi - li - ty As we
bear with one an - oth - er As we
dwell-ing place in our hearts As we
E
dim.
A
Put on
E
love.

49. I heard the voice of Jesus say

Horatius Bonar

'Kingsfold'
Traditional English melody
Arr. Betty Pulkingham

Flowing
Em
Am (+6)
Em
D
G
Am
1. I — heard the voice of Je - sus say, 'Come un - to me — and rest;
heard the voice of Je - sus say, 'Be - hold, I free - ly give
heard the voice of Je - sus say, 'I — am this dark world's light;
*
D
C
D
Em
D
Lay — down, thou wea - ry one, lay down Thy —
The — liv - ing wa - ter; thirst - y one, Stoop
Look un - to me, thy morn shall rise, And —
l.h.
G
Am
Em
Bm7
Em
head up - on — my breast.' I — came to Je - sus
down and drink, and live.' I — came to Je - sus
all thy day — be bright.' I — looked to Je - sus

Am (+6) Em C Maj7 D
as I was, Wea - ry and — worn and sad; I —
and I drank Of — that life - giv - ing stream; My —
and I found In — him my — star, my sun; And —
C D G D G Am
found in him — a — rest - ing place, And — he has made me
thirst was quenched, my — soul re - vived, And — now I live — in
in that light — of — life I'll walk 'Til — trav'- ling days are
Em
1-2.
3.
glad.
him.
done.
2. I —
3. I —
Rit. and dim. . . . .

*The obligato (stems up) may be played by a flute or by a solo stop on the organ.

50. There is power in the blood

Verses: Gary Miles
Refrain: L. E. Jones
Verses: Gary Miles
Refrain: L. E. Jones
With warmth and tenderness
G
D7
1. My Je - sus, he saves and heals me, my
2. He fills me to o - ver flow - ing, he
3 Our Fa - ther, he made and loves us, he
C
D7
G
bo - - - - - - dy, spi - rit, soul. My
comes as the dove, My
gave his on - ly son. We'll
G7
C
Am
king and my shep- herd leads me and
spi - rit and his u - ni - ted. Oh,
see him one day in glo - ry and
D
D7
G
Refrain
makes my bo - dy whole.
won - - - - - - drous, pre-cious love. Oh, there is
join the Three in One.

G
G7
C
G
power, power, won - der- work - ing power in the
D
D7
G
G7
blood of the Lamb. There is power, power,
C
G
D7
G
won - der work-ing power in the pre - cious blood of the Lamb.

51. The man of Galilee

Linda Rich
Arr. Betty Pulkingham

With an easy swing
G
Em
Am7
1. They say that I'm a dream-er, ___ blind and can-not
2. They say that I'm an i - deal-ist, ___ blind and can-not
D7
G
Em
see that ___ life con - sists of liv - ing ___ on-
see that the prin - ci - ples I cling to ___ can't
Am7
D
G
ly to earn mon - ey. Well, you know who I
stand re - a - li - ty. Well, I know who you

Em
Am7
D7
G
am, Lord;
are, Lord;
you'll al - ways care for me.
I on - ly want to
Em
Am
D7
G
be like the man of Gal - i - lee.
Refrain
D7
G
G7
I want to
be
walk
like,
I want to
C
G
hear
talk
like,
I want to
see
be
like
the
1. D7
2. D7
G
Fine
man of Gal - i -
man of Gal - i - lee.

52. Wind, wind

Jane and Betsy Clowe — Jane Clowe

Smooth and sustained

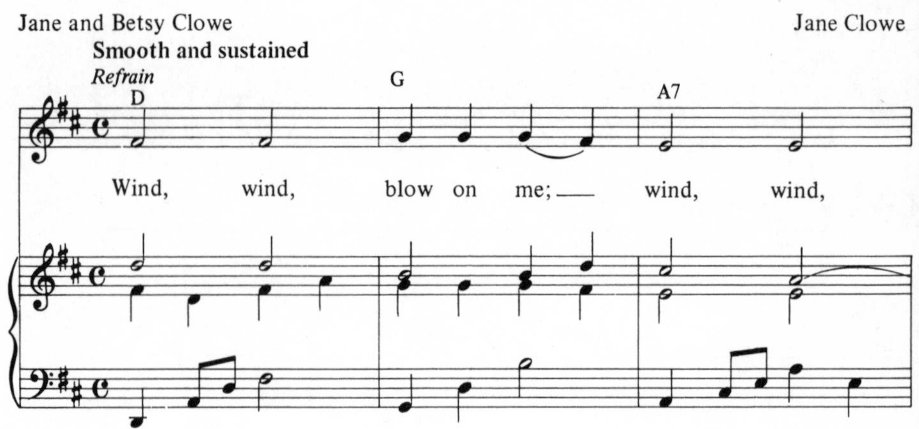
Refrain
D
G
A7
Wind, wind, blow on me; wind, wind,

D
G
Em
set me free; wind, wind, my Fa - ther sent the

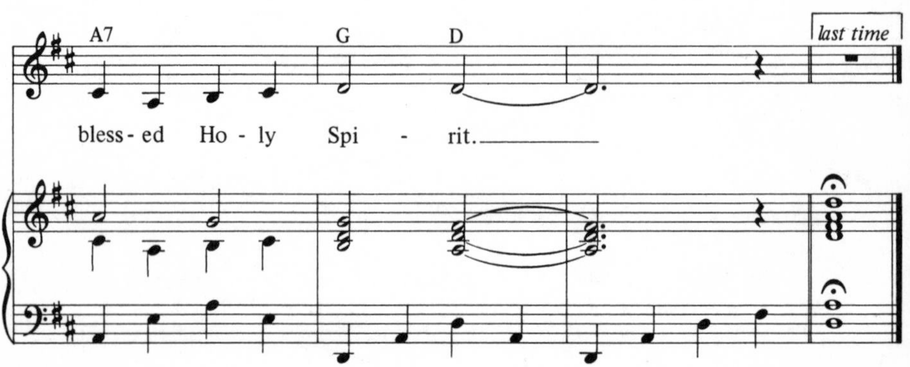
A7
G
D
last time
bless - ed Ho - ly Spi - rit.

D
G
A7
1. Je - sus told us all a - bout you, how we could not
2. When we're wea - ry you con - sole us; when we're lone - ly
3. When un - to the Church you came, it was not in your own but
4. Set us free to love our bro - thers; set us free to
D
G
live with - out you, with his blood the
you en - fold us; when in dan - ger
Je - sus' name. Je - sus Christ is
live for oth - ers that the world the
Em
A7
D
D.C.
pow - er bought to help us live the life he taught.
you up - hold us, bless - ed Ho - ly Spi - rit.
still the same, he sends the Ho - ly Spi - rit.
Son might see and Je - sus' name ex - alt - ed be.
D.C.

53. The fruit of the Spirit

Capo 1 (E)
Refrain: Gal. 5: 22-23
Brian Casebow
Flowing
Refrain
F(E) Bb(A) F(E)
For the fruit of the Spi-rit is love, joy, peace, pa-tience, kind-ness,
Bb(A) C7(B7) F(E) Dm(C#m) Bb(A) F(E)
good - ness, faith-ful-ness, gen-tle-ness, self - con - trol; for
Bb(A) C7(B7) F(E) *Fine* Gm(F#m)
such there is no law.
1. Have you seen my Lord on the
2. Have you seen his face and the
3. Can we an - swer him? Can the
Dm(C#m) C7(B7) F(E)
cross so high? Do you know his name? Do you hear his cry? 'Fa-ther,
look he gave to the dy - ing man he a - lone would save? 'Sin-ner,
heart re - ply? How to fol - low him as we live and die! 'Je-sus,
Gm(F#m) Dm(C#m) Gm(F#m) C7(B7) F(E)
here's my love. Fa-ther, take my love, as the tree bears fruit for you'.
here's my love. Sin-ner, take my love, as the tree bears fruit for you'.
here's our love. Je-sus, take our love, as the tree bears fruit for you'.

54. By their fruits ye shall know them

Capo 3 (C)
Based on Matt. 7: 16

Jon Wilkes
Arr. Betty Pulkingham

With quiet simplicity
Refrain
Eb(C)
Ab(F)
Eb(C)
Can men gath-er grapes from the thorns, or
Fm(Dm)
Bb(G)
(mel.)
figs from the thistl - ed stem?
Eb(C)
Gm(Em)
Cm(Am)
v. 3 (solo) Fa - ther, for - give, they know not what they do;
He that hath ears let him hear,

Copyright © 1972, G.I.A. Publications, Inc.
Used by permission.

A♭(F)
B♭(G)
E♭(C)
last time
by their fruits ye shall know them.
last time
Verses
E♭(C)
Gm(Em)
Cm(Am)
1. My friend came to man to show him how to love; his
2. In dark-ness they led him to priests and kings, they
3. They nailed his hands and split his side, they
4. Bro-thers, oh, judge the heart of man-kind, the
(hum)
A♭(F)
B♭(G)
bless-ing he gave to the meek. But
called him the Lord of the flies.
cast the lots for his clothes.
test is sure and true.

E♭(C)
Gm(Em)
Cm(Am)
men took his love and they called it a lie, his
Spat in his face and they crowned him with thorns:
The on - ly com-fort they had to give was
Eat of the fruit and sa - vour the taste.
A♭(F)
B♭(G)
Refrain
an - swer was on - ly this cry:
'Hail, the King of the Jews.'
vin - - e - gar and gall.
What does it say to you?
A♭(F)
B♭ (G)
E♭(C)
by their fruits ye shall know them.

55. My God

(A psalm of spring)

Capo 1 (E)

Nan Pagano

With warmth
Refrain
F(E)
C7(B7)
Bb(A)
F7(E7)
Fine
My God makes the flow-ers to bloom. My God sends the rain.— My God sets the rain-bow in the sky,— hears each ba-by when he cries,— and each mo-ther as she sighs,— sent his on-ly Son to die.— Oh, praise him, my God is the on-ly true and liv-ing God and he has made me his child.

F(E)
C7(B7)
1. One day in spring while walk-ing with the Lord,
world and I have gi - ven it to you, ev' - ry
2. When sum-mer heat re-veals the cir-cum-stance of life, the
comes and all your world is turn-ing brown, the
3. He spoke a - gain and said,'You are a child of mine, a
out, 'I see, it's all a gift from thee! Let the
1.
F(E)
list - 'ning to his word, I heard him say, 'This is my
bur - den and the strife, call on my name. Then aut-umn
branch up - on the vine. Bring forth my fruit.' My heart cried
2.
F(E)
col - our, ev' - ry hue, ev' - ry breeze and drop of dew is from my
leaves are fall-ing down and win-ter's cold is all a - round. It's from my
sea-sons have their way, Lord, walk with me through night and day. It's from your

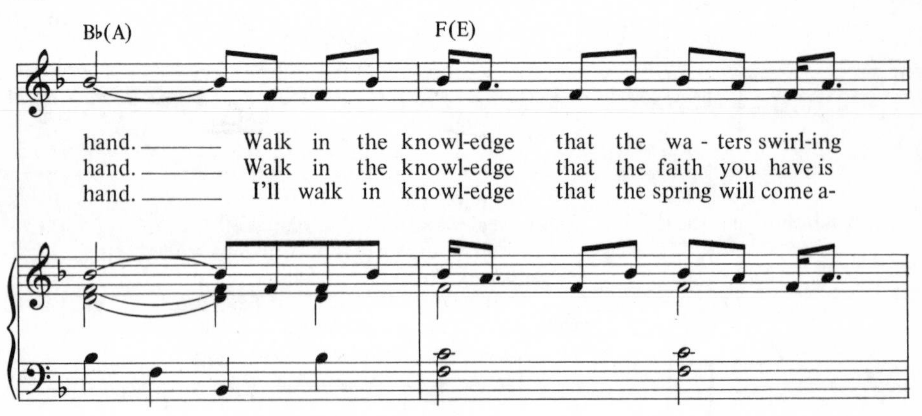
Bb(A)
F(E)
hand. ——— Walk in the knowl-edge that the wa - ters swirl-ing
hand. ——— Walk in the knowl-edge that the faith you have is
hand. ——— I'll walk in knowl-edge that the spring will come a-

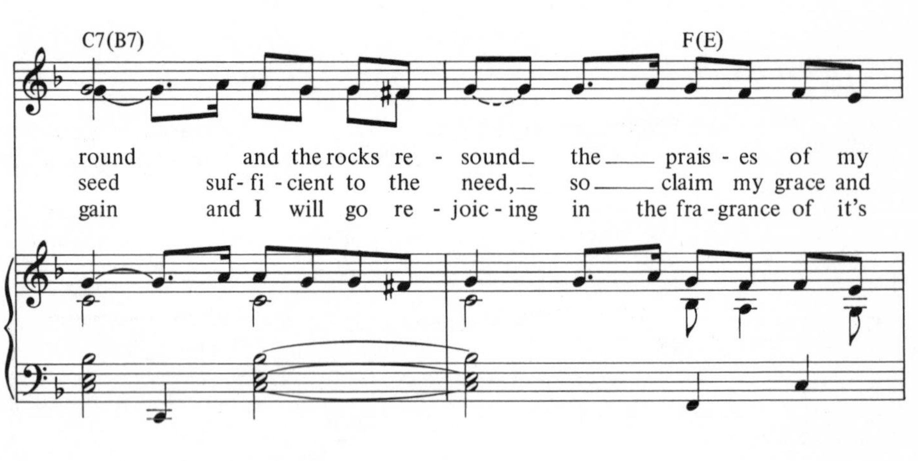
C7(B7)
F(E)
round and the rocks re - sound the —— prais - es of my
seed suf- fi - cient to the need, so —— claim my grace and
gain and I will go re - joic - ing in the fra - grance of it's

D.S.
name. ———
live!' ———
bloom.' ———
My heart cried, my God makes the flow-ers to bloom.
D.S.

56. Israel is my vineyard

Isaiah 27 : 2-3
Capo 2 (Em)

Marie Malone

Smoothly
F♯m(Em)
E(D)
F♯m(Em)
Is - rael is my vine - yard and I, the___ Lord, will

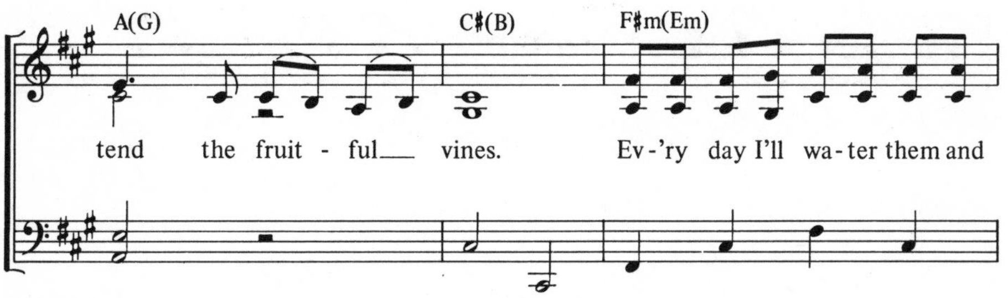
A(G)
C♯(B)
F♯m(Em)
tend the fruit - ful___ vines. Ev-'ry day I'll wa-ter them and

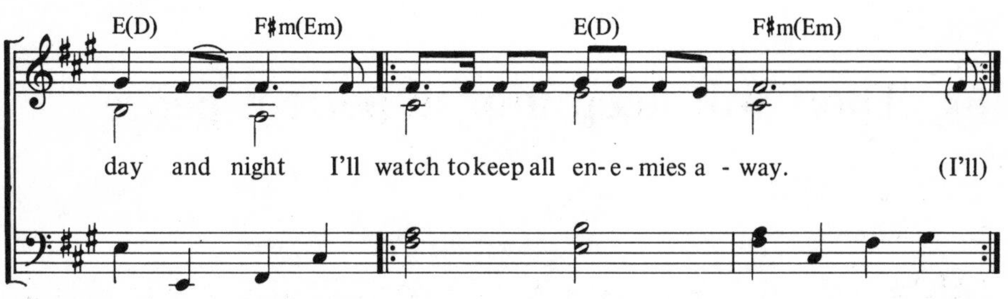
E(D)
F♯m(Em)
E(D)
F♯m(Em)
day and night I'll watch to keep all en-e-mies a - way. (I'll)

F♯m(Em)
E(D)
F♯m(Em)
E(D)
Al-le-lu-ia, al-le-lu-ia, praise the Lord! Al-le-lu-ia, praise his name!

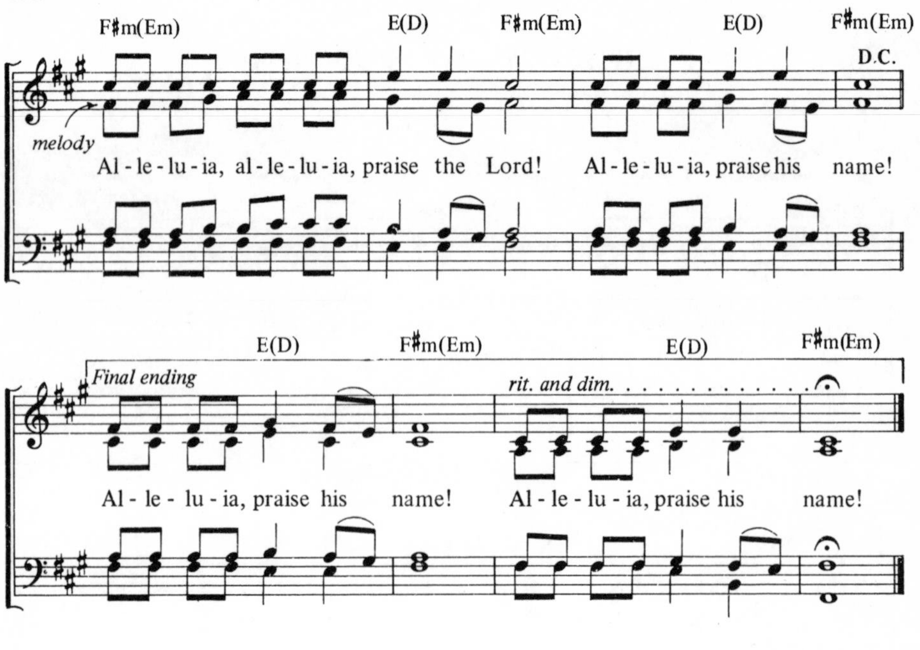
F♯m(Em)
E(D)
F♯m(Em)
E(D)
F♯m(Em)
D.C.
melody
Al - le - lu - ia, al - le - lu - ia, praise the Lord! Al - le - lu - ia, praise his name!
E(D)
F♯m(Em)
E(D)
F♯m(Em)
Final ending
rit. and dim.
Al - le - lu - ia, praise his name! Al - le - lu - ia, praise his name!

57. Thou wilt keep him in perfect peace

Anon.
Arr. Paul Beckwith

Quietly
A
D
A
E
Descant 3. Though your sins as scar - let be, Though your
1. Thou wilt keep him in per - fect peace, Thou wilt keep him in
2. Mar - vel not that I say un - to you, Mar - vel not that I
3. Though your sins as scar - let be, Though your sins as

E7
A
sins — as scar - let be, Though — your
per - fect peace, Thou — wilt keep him in
say un - to you, Mar - vel not that I
scar - let be, Though — your sins — as
A7
D
A
E
A
sins — as scar - let be, They shall — be white — as snow.
per - fect peace Whose mind is stayed on thee.
say un - to you, Ye must be born a - gain.
scar - let be, They shall be white as snow.

4. If the Son shall make you free,
   If the Son shall make you free,
   If the Son shall make you free,
   Ye shall be free indeed.

5. They that wait upon the Lord,
   They that wait upon the Lord,
   They that wait upon the Lord,
   They shall renew their strength.

6. Whom shall I send and who will go?
   Whom shall I send and who will go?
   Whom shall I send and who will go?
   Here I am, Lord, send me.

SECTION 5

SONGS OF THE KINGDOM

THE BODY OF CHRIST

58. The Lord is a great and mighty king

Diane Davis

Lively
Refrain
E
A
E
The Lord is a great and might - y king,
A
B7
just and gen-tle with ev - e - ry thing.
E
A
E
So with hap - pi - ness we sing,

B7
E
1-3
E A E
final ending
and let his prais - es ring.
ring.

A
E
1. We are his voice, we his song;
2. We are his bo - dy here on earth;
3. For our Lord we will stand,
4. The Lord our God is one,

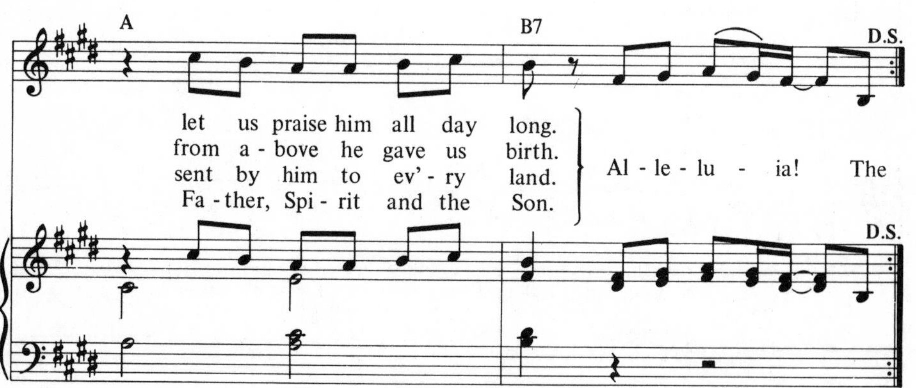
A
B7
D.S.
let us praise him all day long.
from a - bove he gave us birth.
sent by him to ev' - ry land.
Fa - ther, Spi - rit and the Son.
Al - le - lu - ia! The
D.S.

59. This is the feast

John Ylvisaker
Arr. Betty Pulkingham

Majestically
Refrain
F G C G Am
This is the feast of vic-t'ry for our God, for the
Dm G C G Am F G
Lamb who was slain has be-gun his reign: Al - le - lu -
E C Am Dm G C
1-2 3.
ia. ia.
1. Wor - thy is Christ, the Lamb who was slain, whose
2. Sing with all the peo - ple of God and
F G C Am F G
blood set us free— to be peo-ple of God. Pow - er, rich - es,
join in the hymn of all cre - a - - - - - -tion: 'Bless - ing, hon - our,
Em Am Dm G C Am
wis - dom and strength,- and hon - our,— bless - ing and glo - ry are his. This
glo - ry and might be to God and the Lamb— for - ev - er. A - men.' This

60. Please break this bread, Lord

Tender and lyrical

Jodi Page

Refrain
G
Am7
Please break this bread, Lord,
D
G
please break this bread, bread of your
Am7
D
G
bo-dy risen in us.
Am7
D
Pour out your wine, Lord, pour out
G
your wine.
Let it flow

Am7
D
G
last time
through us
to a thirst-y world.
C
D
1. We've come to eat your bread, make us
mem'-ry of your death to give you
2. Let us be bro-ken, O Lord, to feed your
Spi-rit and life that sat-is-
G
C
1.
one. We've come to drink your
thanks. We've come to
sheep. Let us be poured out, O
fy, that you are
D
G
wine, make us one. We've come to
Lord, that men may see that you are

Verse 1
1.
C
D
G
D.C.
cel-e - brate your life and give you praise.
D.C.
Verse 2
2C
D
G
D.C.
ris - en in us to set men free.
D.C.
last time
Am7
D
Please break this bread, Lord, please break this
G
Am7
bread. Pour out your wine, Lord,
D
rit.
G
pour out your wine.

61. Let us break bread together

Traditional
Arr. Mimi Farra

Warmly
E F♯m G♯m F♯m E F♯m
1. Let us break bread to - geth - er, we are one.
drink wine to - geth - er, we are one.
praise God to - geth - er, we are one.
G♯m F♯m E B7 E F♯ B7
Let us break bread to - geth - er, we are one.
Let us drink wine to - geth - er, we are one.
Let us praise God to - geth - er, we are one.
E B7 E E7 A F♯m
1-3. We are one as we stand with our face to the ris - en
B7 E F♯m G♯m F♯m
Son. Oh, Lord, have mer-cy on us.
E F♯m G♯m F♯m
1-2.
2-3. Let us

E F♯m G♯m F♯m E F♯m G♯m F♯m E A E
3.
us. Lord, have mer-cy on us.

62. Who are my mother and my brothers?

Charles High

With deep feeling

An - y - one who does the will of God,

an - y - one who does the will of God, an - y -

one who does the will of God is my bro - ther,

my sis-ter and mo - - - - - - ther.

63. Triumphant Zion

Philip Doddridge

Gary Miles

Well-accented, not fast
E
1. Tri - um - phant
2. Put all thy
3. No more shall
4. God from on
G
A
G
Zi - on, lift thy head
beau - teous gar - ments on,
foes un - clean in - vade,
high has heard thy prayer,
E
G
A
From dust and dark - ness and the
And let thine ex - cel - lence be
And fill thy hal - lowed walls with
His hand thy ru - ins shall re-

E
G
dead;
Though hum - bled long, a -
known:
Decked in the robes of
dread;
No more shall hell's in -
pair:
Nor will thy watch - ful
A
E
G
wake at length,
And gird thee with thy
right - eous - ness,
The world thy glo - ries
sult - ing host
Their vic - t'ry and thy
mon - arch cease
To guard thee in e -
A
E
1-3.
4.
Sa - viour's strength.
shall con - fess.
sor - rows boast.
ter - nal peace.

64. What could be better?

Brian Howard

Crisp and bright
C
1. What could be bet-ter than to
2. What could be bet-ter than to
3. What could be bet-ter than to
4. What could be bet-ter than to
F C G C
come_ to dine on this bread_ and on__ this wine, the
car-ry the cross that our Lord_ has giv - en us?
live in love with God's ho - ly cho - sen ones,
fol-low the Lord? In this whole wide world, there's no-thing I'm sure. So
F C G
bread of__ life__ and the cup of suf-fer-ing, the bo-dy and blood_ of
Just like his on - ly be - got - ten__ Son, he's cho - sen us__ to
liv - ing to-geth - er in u - ni - ty, and out of that life__ the
fol - low__ him__ we shall sure - ly__ do. Lis-ten he's speak-ing to

C
Je-sus, our King? I be-
car - ry one. I be-
world to feed? I be-
me and you. I be-
F G C
lieve he's o-pened our eyes to real - ly see there's
lieve he's o-pened our eyes to real - ly see there's
lieve he's o-pened our eyes to real - ly see there's
lieve he's o-pened our eyes to real - ly see there's
F G C
noth - ing bet-ter than to come to dine in u - ni - ty.
noth - ing bet-ter than to car-ry the cross in u - ni - ty.
noth - ing bet-ter than to live to-geth-er in u - ni - ty.
noth - ing bet-ter than to fol-low the Lord in u - ni - ty.

65. Guide me, O thou great Jehovah

William Williams

'Cwm Rhondda'
John Hughes

Majestically
1. Guide me, O thou great Je - ho - vah, Pil - grim through this
2. O - pen thou the crys - tal foun-tain Whence the heal - ing
3. When I tread the verge of Jor - dan Bid my anx - ious
bar - ren land; I am weak, but thou art might - y
stream doth flow; Let the fie - ry, cloud - y pil - lar
fears sub - side; Death of death, and hell's des - truc - tion,
Hold me with thy pow'r - ful hand: Bread of hea - ven,
Lead me all my jour - ney through: Strong de- liv - 'rer,
Land me safe on Ca- naan's side: Songs of prais - es,
Bread of hea - ven, Feed me now and ev - er -
Strong de - liv - 'rer, Be thou still my strength and
Songs of prais - es, I will ev - er give to

By permission of Dilys S. Webb.

more, Feed me now and ev - er - more.
shield, Be thou still my strength and shield.
thee, I will ev - er give to thee.

66. God of grace and God of glory

Harry Emerson Fosdick

'Cwm Rhondda'
John Hughes

1. God of grace and God of glory,
On thy people pour thy power;
Crown thine ancient Church's story;
Bring her bud to glorious flower.
Grant us wisdom, grant us courage,
For the facing of this hour. *(repeat)*

2. Lo! the hosts of evil round us
Scorn thy Christ, assail his ways!
From the fears that long have bound us
Free our hearts to faith and praise:
Grant us wisdom, grant us courage,
For the living of these days. *(repeat)*

3. Cure thy children's warring madness,
Bend our pride to thy control;
Shame our wanton, selfish gladness,
Rich in things and poor in soul.
Grant us wisdom, grant us courage,
Lest we miss thy kingdom's goal. *(repeat)*

4. Set our feet on lofty places;
Gird our lives that they may be
Armored with all Christ-like graces
In the fight to set men free.
Grant us wisdom, grant us courage,
That we fail not man nor thee. *(repeat)*

By kind permission of Elinor Fosdick Downs.

67. God, make us your family

Capo 3 (A)

Tim Whipple

With pulsating rhythm

Refrain C (A)
Eb(C)
F(D)
C(A)
Your king - dom come, your will be done,
Eb(C)
F(D)
C(A)
now that we have be - come your sons. Let the
r.h.
Eb(C)
F(D)
C(A)
Eb(C)
prayer of our hearts dail - y be: God,
F(D)
C(A)
Fine
make us your fam - - i - ly.
The
Fm(Dm)
Cm(Am)
1. eyes of the blind shall be o - pen'd; the
2. ran - som'd of the Lord shall re - turn; the
3. na - tions will see their shame; the

Fm(Dm)
Cm(Am)
ears of the deaf shall hear. The
is-lands will sing his songs at last. The
one true God will be a-dored. They'll
Fm(Dm)
Cm(Am)
chains of the lame will be bro-ken;
chaff from the wheat shall be burned; his
turn from their for-tune and fame; his
Fm(Dm)
G(E)
D.C.
streams will flow in des-erts of fear.
D.C.
king-dom on earth, it shall come to pass.
ho - ly mountain shall be re - stored.
D.C.

Optional refrain for Christmastide:

Laude, Lauda, Laude, Lauda.
Gloria Emmanuel.
} *repeat*

68. Once no people

Based on 1 Peter 2: 9-10
Maggie Durran

Betty Pulkingham

Bold, well-accented
Refrain
Am
Em
Am
For we are a cho - sen race, a roy - al priest-hood,
G
Am
G
last time
F Maj7
G
ho - ly na - tion. Once no peo-ple, now God's peo-ple, pro-
8
Am
G
A
claim - - ing his mar - - - - vel-lous light.
E

A9
A Maj7
Bm7
1. Sing the songs of faith - ful Zi - on,
2. Dance the steps of joy - ful Zi - on,
3. Taste the fruit of peace - ful val - leys,
4. We will serve through trib - u - la - - - tion,
A
Esus4
we are the stars and the grains of sand.
cym-bals harps and tam - bour-ines.
sip of the wine and eat the bread.
we will fol - low to the cross.
A9
A Maj7
Bm7
Through our faith we are made glo - - ri - ous;
Blow the trum - pet, sound the glo - - - ry
Know the shep - herd who is guid - - -ing,
Know the death and pain of suf - - fer - ing;

A
E sus4
we are sons of A - bra - ham.
in the pres - ence of the Lord.
the Lord, the Lamb of God.
God wipes the tears from our eyes.
E
F Maj7
D.C.
Now God's
light
D.C.
G
peo - ple
Am
G
pro - claim - - - - ing his mar - - - vel-lous
A
light.
8
8

69. Comfort ye

Clint Taylor
Arr. Betty Pulkingham
Gently
Refrain
G C G
Com-fort ye, com-fort ye, my peo - ple.
D C G
Thus saith the Lord.
Fine
D C G D
1. Bear each oth - er up in your times of trou - ble strength-en your-
2. Love one an - oth - er as I have loved you, ev'-ry-thing
3. Bless the Lord for his great mer - cy, es- pe-cially for his
C G
selves in your times of peace.
else will fall in - to place.
Son Je - sus Christ.
D.C.

4. By my spirit you have great power
   which enables you to do my work.

70. Wherever two or more

Smoothly and simply
Brian Howard
Refrain
E
B7
Wher - ev - er two or more are gath-ered in my name, there I am,
E
there I am; wher - ev - er two or more are gath-ered in my name,
B7
A B7
Fine
E
A
there I am in the midst of them.
1. Be - hold what man-ner of
2. If we walk in the light as
E
B7
E
E7
love the Fa-ther gives that we should be called the sons of God. And
he is in the light, we shall al - ways live with him;
A
E
F#
F#7
B7
D.C.
now lit-tle child-ren, a - bide in the Lord; we shall all be like him.
for the blood of Je - sus Christ sets us free from sin.

SECTION 6

SUFFER - REIGN

SONGS OF FAITH AND VICTORY

71. In the name of Jesus

Anon.
Arr. Betty Pulkingham

Victoriously
E
In the name of Je - sus, in the name of Je - sus

B7
we have the vic - to - ry.

In the name of Je - sus, In the name of Je - sus

E
E7
de- mons will have to flee.
A
E
Who can tell what God can do?
B7
E
B7
E
E7
Who can tell of his love for you?
A
E
In the name of Je - sus, Je - sus,
A
B7
E
we have the vic - to - ry.

72. Fight the good fight

John S. B. Monsell

'Old Clarendonian'
Olwen Wonnacott

With vigour
1. Fight the good fight with all thy— might,
2. Run the straight race through God's good— grace,
3. Cast care a - side,— lean on thy guide,
Christ is thy strength and Christ thy right;
Lift up thine eyes and seek his face;
His bound-less mer - cy will pro - vide;
Lay hold on life, and
Life with its way be-
Trust, and thy trust - ing
it shall be thy joy— and crown e - ter - nal-ly.
fore us lies,— Christ is the path and Christ the prize.
soul shall prove— Christ is its life and Christ its love.

4. Faint not, nor fear, his arms are near;
He changeth not, and thou art dear;
Only believe, and thou shalt see
That Christ is all in all to thee.

73. Jesus is a-drivin' out Satan

Capo 3 (Am)
Mary Ackroyd
Arr. Betty Pulkingham
Bold, blues feeling
Cm(Am)
Eb(C)
1. Je - sus is a-driv - in' out Sa - tan from
2. Je - sus is a might - y war - rior, he
3. He gives us his blood and bo - dy; in
4. You win the bat - tle for us,
F (D)
Cm(Am)
ev' - ry-where un - - der the sun.
teach - es us how to fight. 'Take my
his strength we must rest. We
we claim the pow - er you give.
3
Eb(C)
Je - sus is a - driv - in' out Sa - tan, you'd bet - ter
shield and my hel - met and my dou - ble edged sword.' Sa - tan
aren't the ones who fight the bat - tle when
We are your lov - in' peo - ple, and

F(D)
Cm(Am)
get up Sa - tan and run.
fades in the sight of the right.
by your word we will live.
Sa - tan puts us to the test.
Refrain
Cm(Am)
Eb(C)
Je - sus is the vic - tor, Je - - sus, God's son. Je-
F(D)
Cm(Am)
- sus is the king, the bat - tle is won.
Cm(Am)
Eb(C)
Je - sus is the vic - tor, Je - - sus, God's son. Je-
F(D)
Cm(Am)
sus is the king, the bat - tle is won.

74. Faith is the victory

Refrain: John Yates
Verses: Betty Pulkingham

Refrain: Ira Sankey
Verses: Betty Pulkingham

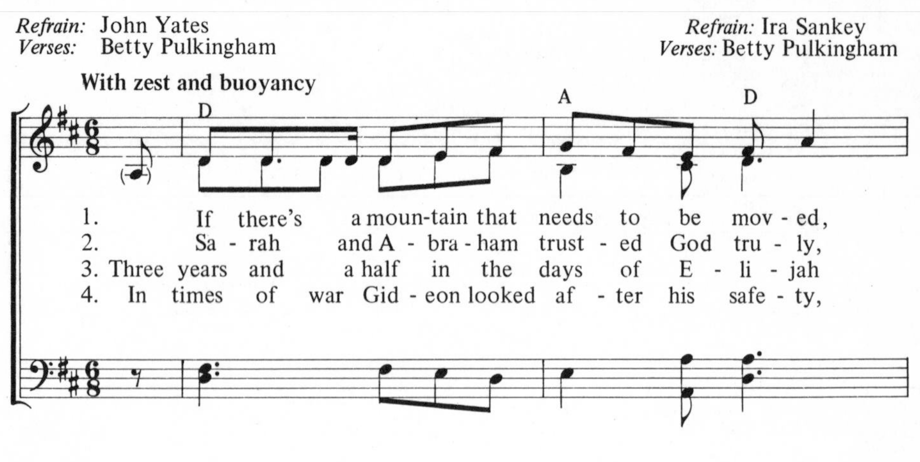
With zest and buoyancy
D A D
1. If there's a moun-tain that needs to be mov - ed,
2. Sa - rah and A - bra - ham trust - ed God tru - ly,
3. Three years and a half in the days of E - li - jah
4. In times of war Gid - eon looked af - ter his safe - ty,

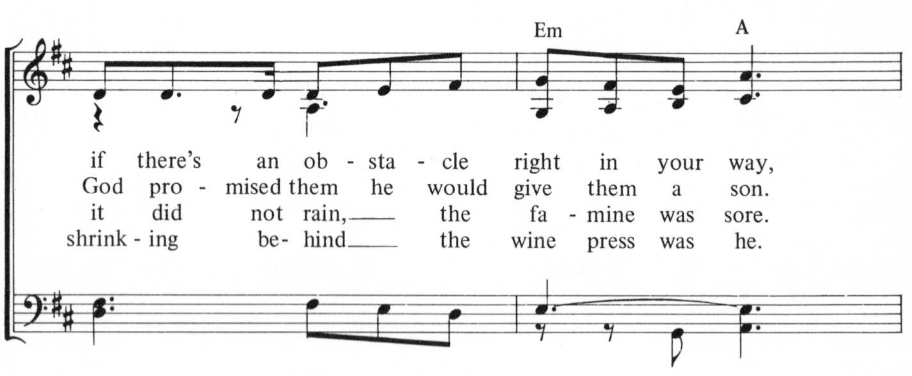
Em A
if there's an ob - sta - cle right in your way,
God pro - mised them he would give them a son.
it did not rain, the fa - mine was sore.
shrink - ing be - hind the wine press was he.

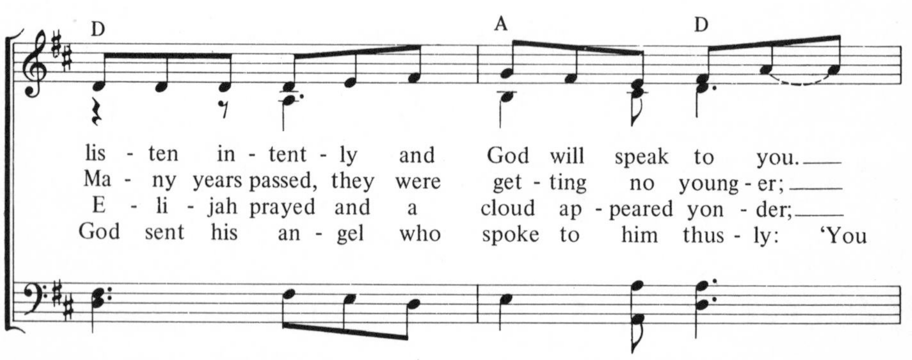
D A D
lis - ten in - tent - ly and God will speak to you.
Ma - ny years passed, they were get - ting no young - er;
E - li - jah prayed and a cloud ap - peared yon - der;
God sent his an - gel who spoke to him thus - ly: 'You

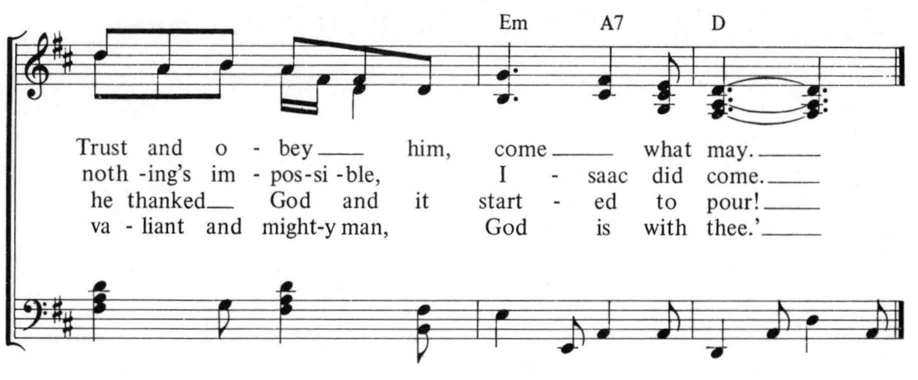
Em A7 D
Trust and o - bey him, come what may.
noth -ing's im - pos-si -ble, I - saac did come.
he thanked God and it start - ed to pour!
va - liant and might-y man, God is with thee.'

Refrain
D A D
Faith is the vic - to-ry. Faith is the vic - to-ry.

G D A7 D
Oh, glo-ri - ous vic - to-ry that o - ver-comes the world.

75. When I survey the wondrous cross

Capo 4 (C)

Isaac Watts

Mikel Kennedy

Smooth, with a 'blues' feeling
EMaj 7 (C Maj7)
F♯m7(Dm7)
G♯m7(Em7)
1. When I sur - vey the won - drous cross
2. For - bid it, Lord, that I should boast
3. See from his head, his hands, his feet,
4. Were the whole realm of na - ture mine,

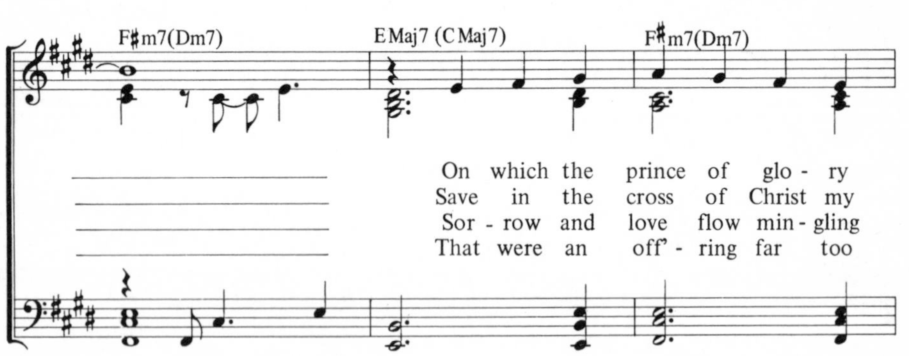
F♯m7(Dm7)
EMaj7 (C Maj7)
F♯m7(Dm7)
On which the prince of glo - ry
Save in the cross of Christ my
Sor - row and love flow min - gling
That were an off' - ring far too

G♯m7(Em7)
F♯m7(Dm7)
E Maj7 (C Maj7)
died, My rich - est
God; All the vain
down; Did e'er such
small; Love so a-

F♯m7(Dm7)
G♯m7(Em7)
F♯m7(Dm7)
gain I count but loss,
things that charm me most,
love and sor - - row meet,
maz - - ing, so di - vine,
A(F)
Am7(Fm7)
E Maj7 (C Maj7)
And pour con - tempt on all my pride.
I sac - ri - fice them to his blood.
Or thorns com - pose so rich a crown?
De-mands my soul, my life, my all.
F♯m7(Dm7)
G♯m7(Em7)
F♯m7(Dm7)
1, 2, 3.
E Maj7 (C Maj7)
Final ending
Rit. and dim.

76. I am persuaded

Romans 8: 38-39

Joan Hettenhouser
Arr. Betty Pulkingham

Bold 'blues' rhythm
D
Bm
Em
A
For
D
Bm
Em
A
I am per-suad - ed that neith-er death, nor life, nor
F♯m
G
A
an - gels nor prin - ci - pal - i - ties, nor
D
Bm
Em
A
powers, nor things pre - sent, nor an - y-thing to come, nor

D Bm Em A
height, nor depth, nor an - y oth - er crea- ture shall be
D Bm Em A
a - ble to sep - a - rate us from the love of God,
D Bm Em A D Bm
which is in Christ Je-sus our Lord.
r.h.
Em A D Bm
1.
D Bm Em A D
2.
Praise God!

77. On Jordan's stormy banks

Samuel Stennett
Traditional
Arr. Betty Pulkingham
Wistful, not too slow
Em
Am
1. On Jor - dan's storm - y banks I stand and
2. When shall I reach that hap - py place and
Em
B7
Em
cast a wish - ful eye to Ca - naan's fair and
be for - ev - er blest? When shall I see my
B7
Em
hap - py land where my pos - ses - sions lie.
Fa - ther's face, and in his bo - som rest?
I am
Brightly, a little faster
E
B7
bound for the pro - mised land, I am
E
B7
original tempo
Em
bound for the pro - mised land. O who will come and

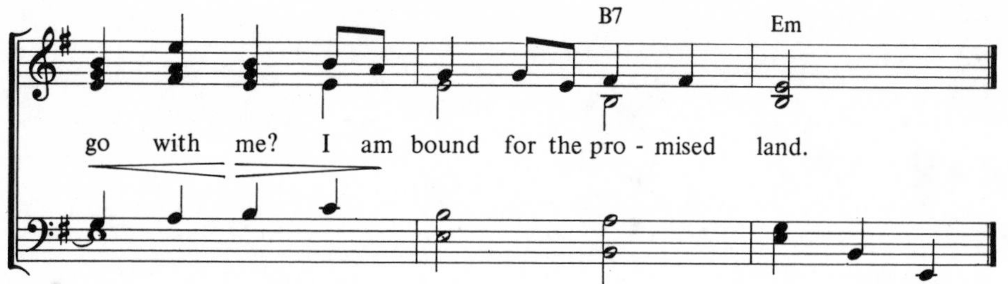
B7
Em
go with me? I am bound for the pro - mised land.

'On Jordan's stormy banks' and *'Come go with me to that land'* (the song that follows) create an unusual medley. Musically, they form a startling contrast; thematically, they make an interesting progression of thought.

78. Come go with me to that land

Traditional
Arr. Betty Pulkingham

Jauntily
E
E7
1. Well come go with me to that land, come go
lov - in' in that land, gon - na be
hon - ey in that land, milk and

A
E
with me to that land, come go with me to that
lov - in' in that land, gon- na be lov - in' in that
hon - ey in that land, milk and hon - ey in that

F♯
B7
land where I'm bound. Come go
land where I'm bound. Gon-na be
land where I'm bound. Milk and
E
E7
A
with me to that land, come go with me to that
lov-in' in that land, gon-na be lov-in' in that
hon-ey in that land, milk and hon-ey in that
C
E
r.h.
land, to that land, to that
land, in that land, in that
land, in that land, in that
Fine
B7
E
A
E
land where I'm bound. 2. There's gon-na be
3. And milk and

Other verses may be added:

Gonna meet Jesus in that land .... Be singin' and dancin' in that land ....
Don't you know heaven is that land?..... *etc.*

79. He is my everything

Capo 1 (E)

Composer and author unknown
Arr. Betty Pulkingham

Worshipfully
F(E) B♭(A) C7(B7) F(E) C7(B7)
He is my ev' - ry-thing, he is my all,
C7(B7) Dm7 (C♯m7) C7(B7) F(E)
he is my ev' - ry- thing, both great and small.
B♭(A) C7(B7) F(E) F7(E7) B♭(A)
He gave his life for me, made ev'ry-thing new.
F(E) C7(B7) F(E)
He is my ev' - ry- thing, he'll sat-is-fy you.

80. There's no greater name

Capo 1 (G)

Michael Baughen

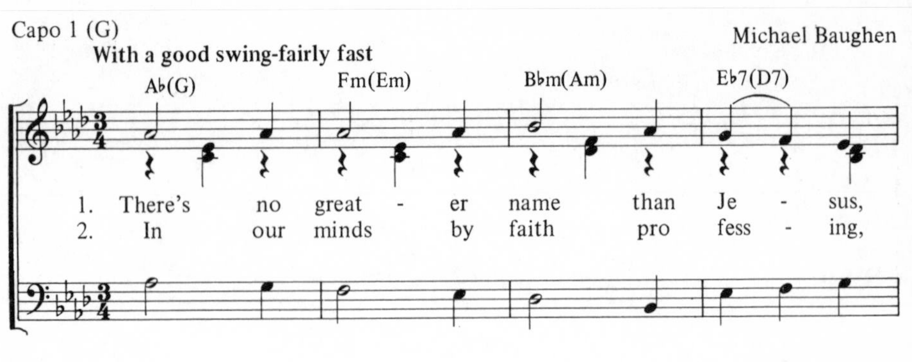

With a good swing-fairly fast
Ab(G) Fm(Em) Bbm(Am) Eb7(D7)
1. There's no great - er name than Je - sus,
2. In our minds by faith pro fess - ing,

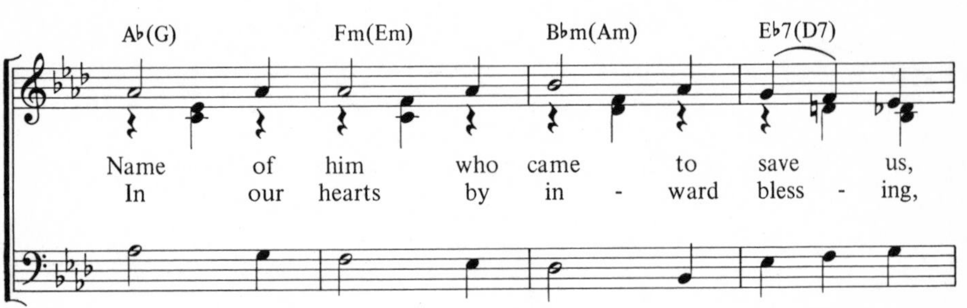

Ab(G) Fm(Em) Bbm(Am) Eb7(D7)
Name of him who came to save us,
In our hearts by in - ward bless - ing,

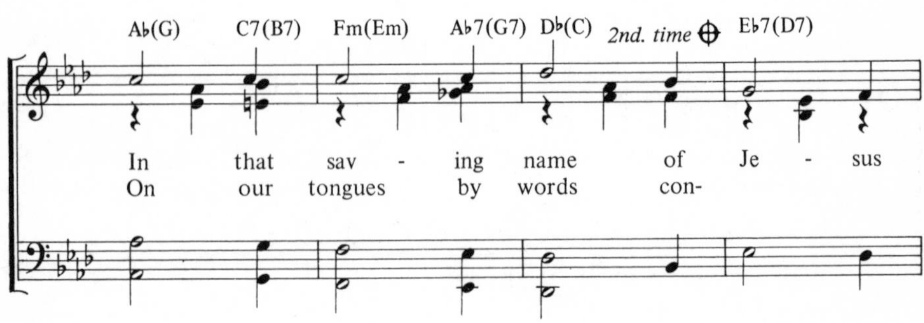

Ab(G) C7(B7) Fm(Em) Ab7(G7) Db(C) 2nd. time Eb7(D7)
In that sav - ing name of Je - sus
On our tongues by words con-

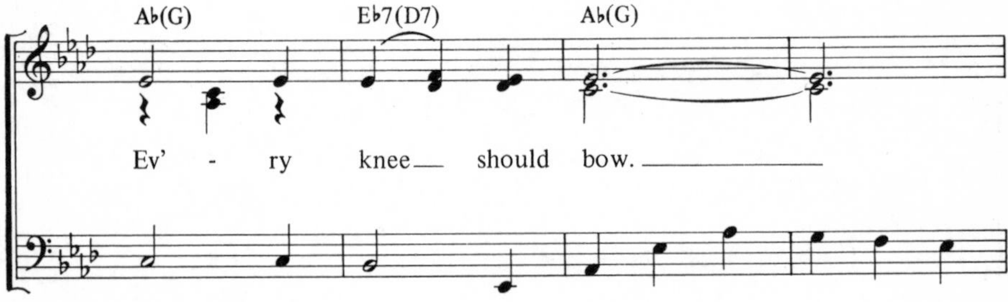

Ab(G) Eb7(D7) Ab(G)
Ev' - ry knee should bow.

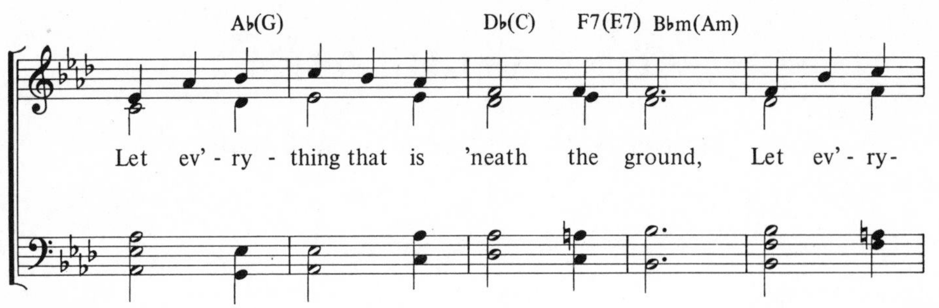
Ab(G)
Db(C)
F7(E7)
Bbm(Am)
Let ev'-ry-thing that is 'neath the ground, Let ev'-ry-

Eb(D)
Eb7(D7)
Ab(G)
thing in the world a-round, Let ev'-ry-thing that's

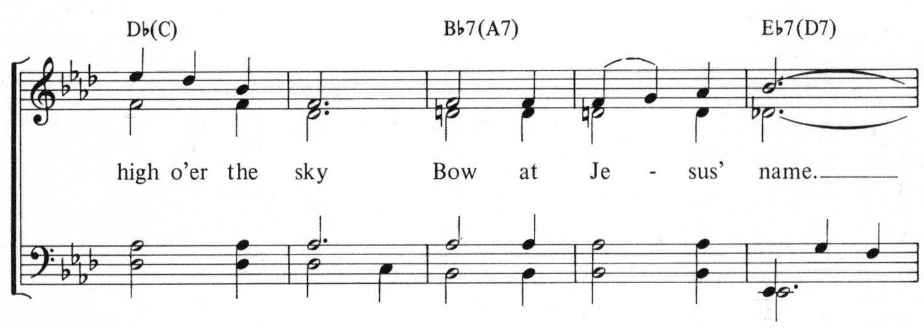
Db(C)
Bb7(A7)
Eb7(D7)
high o'er the sky Bow at Je-sus' name.

2nd. time
D.C.
Eb(D)
Ab(G)
fess-ing Je-sus Christ is Lord!

SECTION 7

COME AS CHILDREN

SONGS FOR CHILDREN OF ALL AGES

81. I am so glad that Jesus loves me

Philipp Bliss
Arr. Betty Pulkingham

Happily
G
D7
G
1. I am so glad that our Father in heav'n
2. Though I forget him and wander away;
3. O if there's only one song I can sing,
D
G
(D7)
G
Tells of his love in the book he has given.
Still he doth love me wherever I stray.
When in his beauty I see the great King,
D7
G
Wonderful things in the Bible I see;
Back to his dear loving arms do I flee,
This shall my song in eternity be,

C
D7
G
This is the dear - est, that Je - sus loves me.
When I re - mem - ber that Je - sus loves me.
O what a won - der that Je - sus loves me.
Refrain
C
I am so glad that Je - sus loves me,
D7
G
Je - sus loves me, Je - sus loves me. I am so glad that
C
D7
G
Je - sus loves me, Je - sus loves ev - en me.

82. (Someone), Jesus loves you

Anon.
Arr. Betty Pulkingham

Simply
(Someone), Je-sus loves you. (Someone), Je-sus loves you. And love, love, love comes a-trickl'-in' down.
Seek and ye shall find, ask an-y-where, give a knock and the door shall be o-pen'd and
love, love, love comes a-trickl'-in' down.
last time, slowly
And love, love, love comes a - trickl' - in' down.

83. Jesus loves Kristi*

(to Kristi)

Capo 1 (E)

Ann House

As a lullaby
F(E)
C7(B7)
Je - sus, Je-sus loves (name). Yes, he does, yes, he does.
F(E)
Je - sus, Je-sus loves (name). Yes, he does, yes, he does.
B♭(A)
B♭m(Am)
Je - sus, Je-sus loves (name). Yes, he does, yes, he does.
F(E)
C7(B7)
F(E)
B♭(A)
F(E)
And he wants (name) to love him too.

* In 1971 Kristi, age 4, went home to her heavenly Father. This song, composed by her mother shortly before her death, was a gift to Kristi, and now it belongs to the whole world.

84. On tiptoe

84.
On tiptoe
Capo 4 (C)
Verses: Maggie Durran
Refrain: Romans 8: 19
Philips Translation
Jodi Page
Arr. Betty Pulkingham
Gracefully
detached
E(C)
B7(G7)
C♯m(Am)
F♯m(Dm)
1. I walk with you, my child-ren, through val - leys filled with gloom; in e - choes of the star - light and sha- dows of the moon. In the
2. I made the mot-tled stickle-back to hide in cry - stal streams, the star - ing owl to scan the night, the can-dle's gen - tle beams; I
3. If life were filled with bub-bles, they'd glis - ten and they'd burst; if life were filled with jew - els they'd line a rich man's purse; but
4. My love for you, my child-ren, puts rain-bows in your hand, born of cloud-ed sor - rows in a sun-burst morn-ing land; they

E(C)
C♯m(Am)
F♯m(Dm)
B7(G7)
whisp-ers of the night-wind are gen - tle words for you to
made the sil - ly cam - el to roam the des - ert sand, but
life is filled with wa - ter that flows from depths of love, it
arch a - bove the smi - ling eyes where tears can still be seen, and a-
E(C)
C♯m(Am)
F♯m(Dm)
B7(G7)
touch you and as - sure you it's my world you're walk-in'
you I made, my child - ren, to walk and hold my
flows to fill your wear - i - ness with bless - - - ing from a-
dorn with gen - tle tremb-ling touch the bride who is my
E(C)
Refrain
C♯m(Am)
through.
hand.
bove.
own.
And all cre - a - tion's strain-ing on

F♯m(Dm) B7(G7) E(C) C♯m(Am)

tip-toe just to see___ the sons of God

F♯m(Dm) B7(G7) E(C) last time

come_ in-to their own.

85. I sing a song of the saints of God

Lesbia Scott

'Grand Isle'
John Henry Hopkins

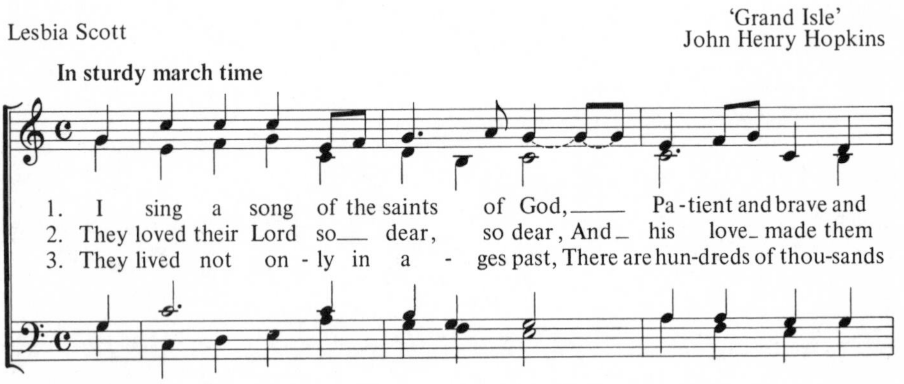
In sturdy march time
1. I sing a song of the saints of God,___ Pa-tient and brave and
2. They loved their Lord so_ dear, so dear, And_ his love_ made them
3. They lived not on-ly in a-ges past, There are hun-dreds of thou-sands

true, Who toiled and fought and lived and died For the
strong; And they fol-lowed the right, for Je - sus' sake, The
still, The world is bright with the joy - ous saints Who
Lord they loved and knew. And one was a doc - tor, and
whole of their good lives long. And one was a sol - dier, and
love to do Je - sus' will. You can meet them in schools, or in
one was a queen, And one was a shep-herd-ess on the green: They were
one was a priest, And one was slain by a fierce wild beast: And there's
lanes or at sea, In church or in trains, or in shops or at tea, For the
all of them saints of God and I mean, God help - ing, to be one too.
not a - ny rea - son, no, not the least, Why I shouldn't be one too.
saints of God are just folk like me, And I mean to be one too.

86. Knock, knock

'Ask and it shall be given you'

Based on Luke 11: 9-13
Betty Pulkingham
Playfully
Refrain
D G D
Ask, and it shall be giv - en you. Seek, and ye shall
Knock on wood:
A D G
find.___ If you knock, knock, knock, the door will
D A7 D *Fine*
o - pen un - to you ev'- ry time.
Verses
G
1. If a son shall
2. If a son shall
3. If a son shall
D G D
ask his fa - ther___ for a piece of bread,
ask his fa - ther___ for a lit - tle fish,
ask his fa - ther for an egg___ o - ver light,

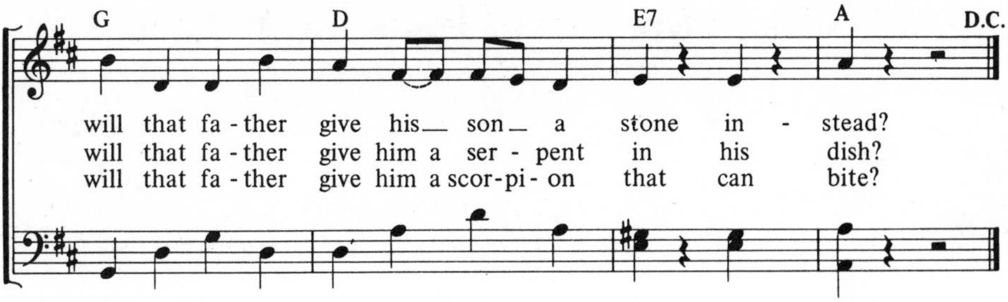

will that fa - ther give his son a stone in - stead?
will that fa - ther give him a ser - pent in his dish?
will that fa - ther give him a scor-pi - on that can bite?

D.C.

Verse 4.

Smoothly

4. If ye then, be - ing e - vil, know how to give good things,
How much more your lov - ing hea-ven-ly Fa - ther brings! Your
lov - ing hea-ven-ly Fa - ther brings the best gift of all! He
gives the Ho - ly Spi - rit un - to them that call on him.

D.C.

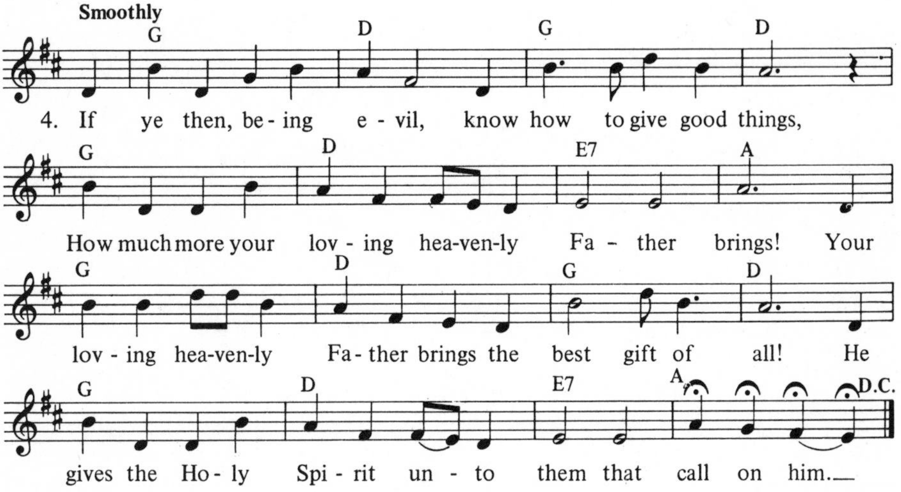

87. Pullin' the weeds, Lord*

Max Dyer

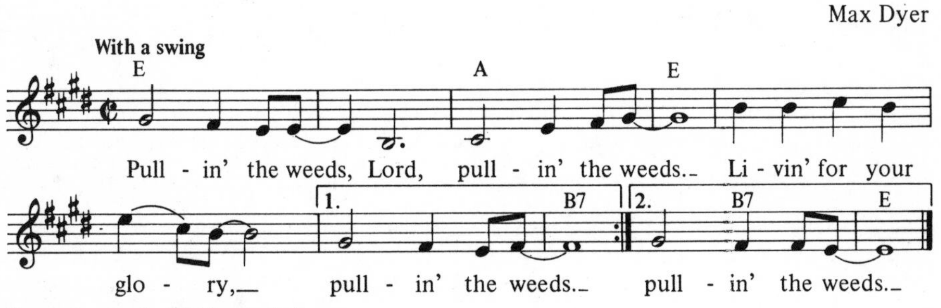
With a swing
E
A
E
B7
1.
2.
Pull - in' the weeds, Lord, pull - in' the weeds. Li - vin' for your
glo - ry, pull - in' the weeds. pull - in' the weeds.

* a work song for 'children' of all ages.

Other suggested verses:

Sweepin' the floor, Lord.......
Goin' to school (church, bed, *etc!*), Lord.......
Singin' this song, Lord.......

88. One, two, three, Jesus loves me

Lisa Mazak
(age 9)

Happily
Refrain
E A E A E
One, two, three, Je-sus loves me. One, two,
B7 E Fine E A E
Je-sus loves you. 1. Three, four, he loves you more
A E B7 E D.C. E
than you've ev-er been loved be-fore. 2. Five, six, seven, we're
A E A E B7 E D.C.
go-ing to heav'n. Eight, nine, it's tru-ly di-vine.
E A E 1. A E
3. Nine, ten, it's time to end; but in-stead we'll
cresc.

B7 E D.C. 2. A E B7 E
sing it a - gain. there's no time to sing it a - gain.
rit. and dim.

89. Put on your boots

Sherrell Prebble

Western Americana

E

1. Come with me ___ to a land where peo - ple are
2. land for now, ___ a land where your spi - rit can
3. There you will find ___ ach - ing souls ___ re-

A E

free, ___ where the lambs and the wolves roam to-
live, ___ and eat the bread ___ of ___
vived, ___ when the lead - er of ___ that

A
B7
geth - er through the coun - try. They
life that makes you whole.
land pass - es by. The
E
v. 2-3
say that a child can ride on a li - on's
When you're thirs - ty and you want a
lone - ly peo - ple find fel - - low-
A
E
back, and not one man steals
drink, they have liv - ing
ship, and there is plen - ty of

A
B7
E
Refrain
food _ from his bro - ther's shack. So
wa - ter for your souls.
heal - ing for the sick.
A
E
put on your boots, let's get on the road. There's
A
B7
1. E
just not that much time, you know.
2. E
D.C.
Final ending
know. 2. It's a

90. Jesus took my burdens

Anon.
Arr. Betty Pulkingham

Happily
E
1. Je-sus took my bur-dens and he rolled them in the sea,
2. Now I am hap-py, hap-py as can be,
B7
rolled them in the sea,
hap-py as can be,
E
rolled them in the sea.
hap-py as can be,
Je-sus took my bur-dens and he rolled them in the sea,
Now I am hap-py, hap-py as can be,
B7
nev-er to re-mem-ber an-y-
nev-er to re-mem-ber an-y-
E
more.
more.

'Jesus took my burdens' may be sung in sequence with the following song.

91. I must have Jesus

Anon.
Arr. Betty Pulkingham

Fast and light
E
B7
E
E7
A
Am
E
B7
E
1. I must have Je - sus in my whole life. I must have
Je - sus in my life. In my walk-ing, in my talk-ing, in my
sleep-ing, in my wak-ing, must have Je - sus in my life.

2. I have Christ Jesus in my whole life.
I have Christ Jesus in my life.
In my walking, in my talking,
In my sleeping, in my waking,
Have Christ Jesus in my life.

92. I'm not alone

Cheerfully
Diane Davis
Refrain
D G A7
I'm not a - lone for my Fa - ther is with me,
D A7
with me wher-ev - er I go.
D G Gm
Speak-ing words of faith, of cour-age and of love, he's
D A7
last time
1-3. D
with me, he loves me wher - ev - er I go.
D G A7
1. Wak-ing in the morn - ing, get - ting read-y for school,
2. And when I find my - self in a mess,
3. All of my life ev' - ry - where that I go,

D
A7
D
walk-ing down the road,
in class, at
I can trust in him,
call on his name and
I will walk with him,
prais-ing him and
G
Gm
D
A7
work, or at play,
watch him move,
bless-ing his name,
he's with me, he loves me wher-ev-er I
D
D.C.
D
go.
go.
he's
A7
with me, he loves me wher-ev-
er I go.

Put on the whole armour of God

'The spiritual war'

Ephesians 6: 10-17

Shirley Lewis Brown

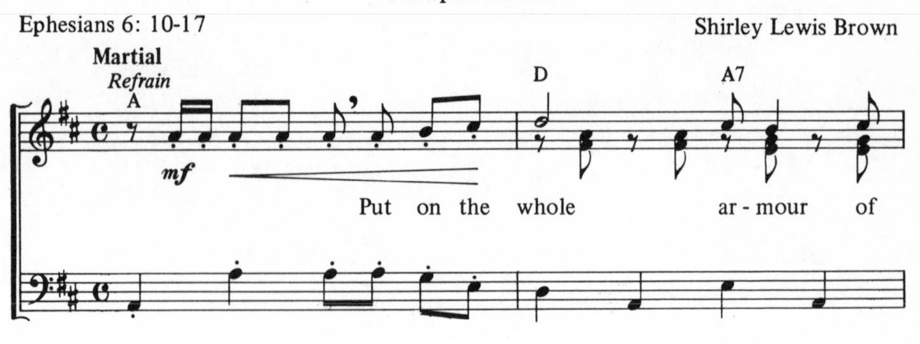
Martial
Refrain
A
D
A7
mf
Put on the whole ar - mour of

D
A
D
God, put on the whole ar-mour of God, put on the

A7
D
whole ar - mour of God, that you may

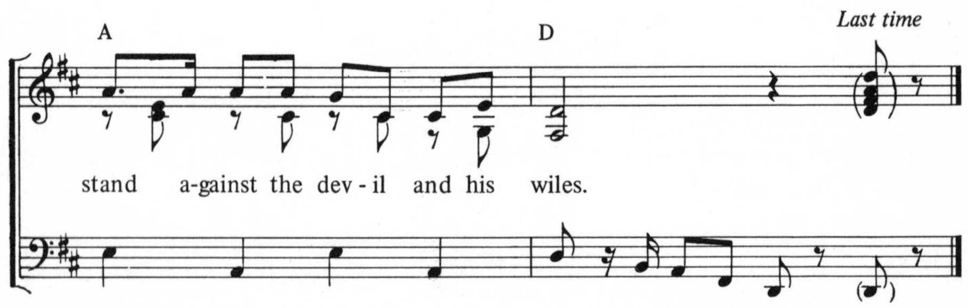
A
D
Last time
stand a-gainst the dev - il and his wiles.

A
E
1. Take your stand with truth as your belt.
2. Put on right-eous- ness for your breast - plate.
3. Shoe your feet with the gos - pel of peace.
4. As your hel - met don sal - va - tion from God.
5. In your hand take the sword of the Spi - rit,
6. A - bove all else take the shield of faith to
A
Take your stand with truth as your belt.
Put on right-eous - ness for your breast - plate.
Shoe your feet with the gos - pel of peace.
As your hel- met don sal - va - tion from God.
Which is real - ly the word of God.
quench all the fier - - - y darts of the wick - ed.
A7
D
Put on the whole ar- mour of

94. Clean hands

Capo 1 (E)

'Bethany'
Lowell Mason
Arr. Betty Pulkingham

Author unknown

Simply
F(E) Bb(A) F(E)
Clean hands or dirt - y hands, brown eyes or
C7(B7) F(E) Bb(A)
blue, pale cheeks or ro - sy cheeks,
F(E) C7(B7) F(E) Bb(A)
Je - sus loves you. Come to him
F(E) Bb(A) F(E) C7(B7)
while you may, be his lit - tle lambs to - day.
F(E) Bb(A) F(E) C7(B7) F(E)
Clean hands or dirt - y hands, Je - sus loves you.

95. Bless you, Jesus

Robert Reynolds

Playfully
E
B7
Bless you, Je - sus, bless you. Bless you, Je - sus,
E
bless you. Bless you, Je - sus, bless you.
B7
E
All the peo-ple now, bless you.

Other verses may be added:

Love you.......... Trust you....... Serve you....... Praise you.......

Last verse:

Amen, Jesus, Amen. *(repeat twice).*
All the people now say, 'Amen.'
(spoken)

96. He's my rock, my sword, my shield

Author unknown
Verse 2: Wendy Rhodes

Composer unknown
Arr. Jeanne Harper

With abandon
D A D D7
1. He's my rock, my sword, my shield, He's the
2. He's my peace, my joy, my love, My name's
G D
wheel in the mid-dle of the wheel; He's the li - ly of the val - ley the
written in his book a - bove, He's the cap-tain of my company in the
E7 A A7 D D7
bright and morn-ing star. Makes no differ - ence what you say, I'm go-ing
bat - tle of the Lord. Makes no difference what the devil may do, I've got
G D A7
on my knees and pray, I'm gon-na see my Lord in glo - ry one of these
vic-try, how a-bout you? I'm gon-na see my Lord in glo - ry one of these

Refrain
D
D7
G
days. ——
days. ——
I'm gon-na see my Lord in glo - ry one of these
D
G
D
G
days. ——
He's the rock of my soul and I'm gon-na sing his
A7
D
D7
praise. (Hal - le - lu - jah) He's my rock, my sword, my shield, He's the
G
D
wheel in the mid - dle of the wheel. I'm gon - na
A7
D
see my Lord in glo - ry one of these days.

SECTION 8

GO FORTH!

SONGS OF OUTREACH

97. Prayer of St. Francis

Sebastian Temple
Arr. Betty Pulkingham

Flowing
D
1. Make me a chan-nel of your peace. Where
2. Make me a chan-nel of your peace. Where
3. Make me a chan-nel of your peace. It
Em
A7
there is hat - red let me bring your love; where
there's des - pair in life let me bring hope; where
is in par - don - ing that we are par - doned, in
Em
there is in - jur - y, your par - don, Lord; and
there is dark - ness, on - ly light; and
giv - ing to all men that we re - ceive; and in

Em7
A7
D
Fine
D7
*
where there's doubt, true faith in you.
where there's sad - ness, ev - er joy.
dy - ing that we're born to e - ter - nal life.
Oh,
G
D
mas - ter, grant that I may nev - er seek so
A7
D
D7
much to be con - soled as to con - sole; to be
G
D
un - der - stood as to un - der - stand; to be
E
E7
A
D.C.
loved, as to love with all my soul.

* Voices may sing in two-part harmony.

98. The light of Christ

Donald Fishel
Arr. Betty Pulkingham

Flowing
Refrain
C
Part 1. The light of Christ has
Part 2. The light of Christ
F Dm G C
come in - to the world, the light of
has come in - to the world, the
F G C 1-3
Christ has come in - to the world.
light of Christ has come.

Verses
F C F G
1. All men must be born a-gain to see the king-dom of
2. God gave up his on-ly Son out of love for the
3. The light of God has come to us so that we might have sal-
C F G C
God; the wa-ter and the Spi-rit bring new
world, so that all men who be-lieve in him will
va-tion; from the dark-ness of our sins we walk in-to
Dm G C
D.C. 4.
life in God's love.
live for ev-er. world.
glo-ry with Christ Je-sus.
D.C.

99. Drop everything and go

Diane Davis

Lightly
Refrain
D
G
D
It makes no dif - fer-ence who you are. It
A7
D
makes no dif - fer-ence where you're go - ing to;
G
D
when Je - sus calls to you,
A
D
A7
D
Fine
drop ev'-ry-thing and go, drop ev'-ry-thing and go.

D G D A A7
1. Pe-ter was a fish-er-man, he was fish-ing in his
2. Laz'-rus was dead and bound, dead and bound in his
3. Je-sus is the Son of God, his Fa-ther called un-to
D G
boat. When Je-sus called to
grave. When Je-sus called to
him, said, 'My peo-ple need to be re-
D A D
him, he dropped ev'-ry-thing and he went, he
him, he dropped all his bonds and he went, he
deemed.' He took up his cross and he went to
A7 D D.C.
dropped ev'-ry-thing and he went.
dropped all his bonds and he went.
die for you and me.
D.C.

100. Let there be peace on earth

Sy Miller and Jill Jackson

Slowly
C Am Dm7 G7 C F
Let there be peace on earth and let it be-
Let peace be - gin with me, let this be the
C Dm G7 C B7
gin with me; Let there be peace on
mo - ment now. With ev' - ry step I
Em G7 2nd. time
earth, the peace that was meant to be, With
take, let this be my sol - emn vow: To
Am Em F G7
God as our Fa - ther, bro - thers all are

C
Am7
D7
G
we,
Let me walk with my bro - ther
Am7
D7
G
G7
in per - fect har - mo ny.
C
C aug.
F
take each mo-ment and live each mo-ment in peace e-
D7
C
E7
F
ter - nal - ly.
Let there be peace on
C
F
Dm7
G7
C
earth and let it be - gin with me.

101. Freely, freely

Carol Owens
Smoothly
E
C♯m
F♯m7
1. God for - gave my sin in Je - sus'
pow'r is giv'n in Je - sus'
B7
F♯m7
B7
name. I've been born a - gain in
name. In earth and heav'n in
E Maj7
E7
A
Je - sus' name. And in Je - sus'
Je - sus' name. And in Je - sus'
E
A
B7
E
name I come to you to
name I come to you to

G♯m F♯m7 B7 E B7

slowly

share his love as he told me to.
share his pow'r as he told me to. } He said

**Refrain a tempo*

E F♯m7 B7

free - ly, free - ly you have re - ceived;

E

free - ly, free - ly give. ______

F♯m7 B7

Go in my name and be - cause you be - lieve,

E 1. 2.

oth - ers will know that I live. ______ 2. All__ __

* For variation, some voices may sing in thirds above the refrain melody, like this:

etc.

102. The Spirit is a-movin'

Carey Landry

Quick tempo, but steady
E
A
E
The Spi - rit is a - mov-in' all o - ver, all

D
E
Fine
o - ver this land.
4. The
r.h.

E
A
1. Peo - ple are gath - er - in', the Church is born, the
2. Doors are o - pening as the Spi - rit comes, his
3. Filled with the Spi - rit we are sent to serve, we are
4. world born once is born a - gain,

E
D
Spi - rit is a - blow - in' on a world re-
fire is burn - ing in his peo - - - - - - ple
called out as bro - thers, we are called to
we re - cre - ate it in love and

E
born.
now.
work.
joy.
The
r.h.

5. Old men are dreaming dreams,
   And young men see the light.

6. Old Walls are falling down,
   And men are speaking with each other.

7. The Spirit fills us with his power
   To be his witnesses to all we meet.

8. The Spirit urges us to travel light
   To be men of courage who spread his fire.

9. God has poured out his Spirit
   On all, on all of mankind.

103. Moto Imeaka

Capo 1 (E)

East African folk song
Arr. Betty Pulkingham

Full and free
F(E)
(Refrain) Mo - - - - - - to im - ea - ka le - o,
(1.) fire is burn- ing in my soul, God's
C(B)
Mo - - - - - - to ni - ka - zi ya Ye - su,
fire is mak - ing me whole, God's
F(E)
Bb(A)
Mo - - - - - - to im - ea - ka le - o, Tu
fire is sweep - ing o'er the earth. Praise
With rhythmic precision and drive
C(B)
C7(B7)
F(E)
im - be Hal - le - lu - jah, Mo - to im - ea - ka, Tu
God, I've got God's fire and it's burn-ing in my soul, Praise

C(B)
C7(B7)
F(E)
Fine
im - be Hal - le - lu - jah, Mo - to im - ea - ka. 1. God's
God. I've got God's fire and it's burn-ing in my soul. (Refrain)

*This song in Swahili is sung throughout East Africa. The literal English translation of the refrain is: 'The fire is burning today, fire is the work of Jesus, the fire is burning today, let us sing Hallelujah, the fire is burning.' The English verse in the musical text has essentially the same meaning. Other suggested verses: 'God's Spirit is burning.....','God's power is burning.....'. The last line may be repeated accumulatively, in reverse order: 'Praise God I've got God's Spirit.....', 'power.....', 'fire.'

104. And ye shall have power

Acts 1: 6-8

Clive Corrin
Arr. Betty Pulkingham

With a lilt

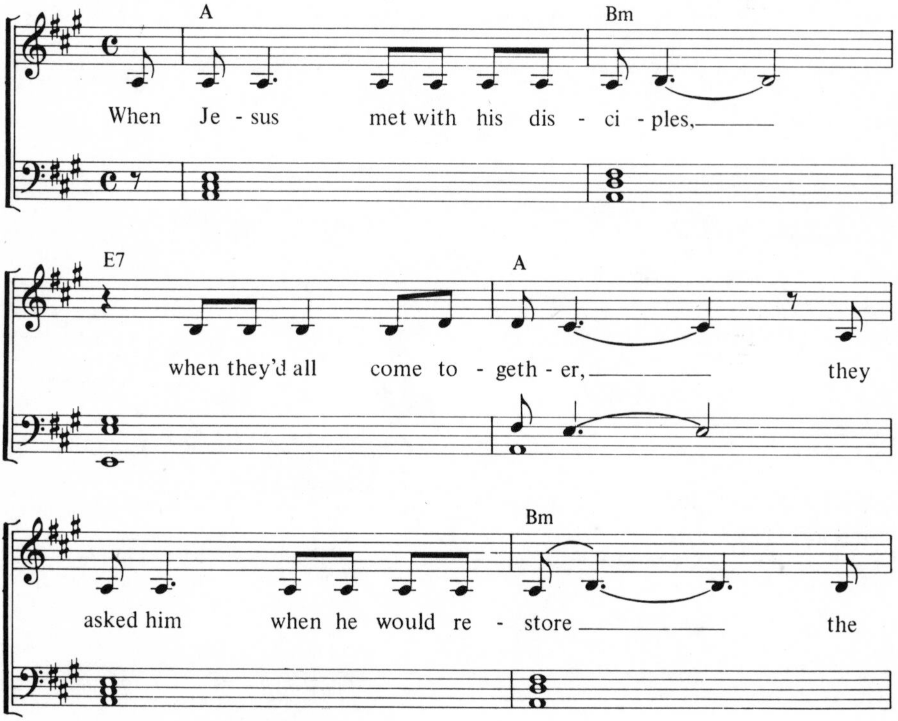

A Bm
When Je - sus met with his dis - ci - ples,____

E7 A
when they'd all come to - geth - er,____ they

Bm
asked him when he would re - store ____ the

E7
A
king - dom
of
Is - rael.
D
He told them that the
time
was
C♯m
not
for them
to
know,
the
D
A
times
and the
sea - sons were his
Fa - ther's,
E7
on - ly
he
would
know.
* A
D
'But
ye
shall
have
pow'r

E7
A
when the Spi - rit comes on you.
D
Ye shall be my wit - ness - es
E7
A
to the ends of the earth;
Bm
to all Je - ru - sa - lem,
E7
A
through all Ju - de - a,
Bm
and in Sa - ma - ri - a,

E7
A
to the ends of the earth.
E7
A
to the ends of the earth.'

105. Come to the waters

With a gentle swing

Jodi Page

Refrain
D
D+4
D
Come to the wa - ters and
A7
D
final ending
I will give you rest.
you will be re - freshed.
r.h.

D
A7
D
1. Je - sus said, 'Come un - to
2. Je - sus said of the wa - ters
3. Je - sus said, 'He who be-
4. So with joy ye shall draw
A7
G
A
me all ye wea - - - - - - - - -
that he gave, he who drinks
lieves in me out of him shall
wa - ter out of wells
D
D.C.
- - - ry, hea - vy la - den.'
shall nev - er thirst a - gain.
flow liv - ing wa - ters.'
of sal - va - tion.
D.C.

106. Jesus! the name high over all

'Lydia'
Charles Wesley
Thomas Phillips

With strength
1. Je - sus! the name high o - ver all,
2. Je - sus! the name to sin - ners dear,
3. Je - sus! the pris - 'ners' fet - ters breaks,

In hell or earth, or sky; An - gels and
The name to sin - ners giv'n; It scat - ters
And brui - ses Sa - tan's head; Pow'r in - to

men be - fore it fall, And de - vils fear and
all their guil - ty fear, It turns their hell to
strength-less souls it speaks, And life in - to the

fly, And de - vils fear and fly.
heav'n, It turns their hell to heav'n.
dead, And life in - to the dead.

4. O that the world might taste and see
   The riches of his grace;
   The arms of love that compass me
   Would all mankind embrace. *(repeat)*

5. His only righteousness I show,
   His saving grace proclaim;
   'Tis all my business here below
   To cry: 'Behold the lamb!' *(repeat)*

6. Happy, if with my latest breath
   I might but gasp his name;
   Preach him to all, and cry in death;
   'Behold, behold the lamb!' *(repeat)*

107. The Spirit of the Lord

Isaiah 61: 1-2

Jim Strathdee

A relaxed and easy tempo
The Spi-rit of the Lord is up-on me, because he has a-noint-ed me to
preach good news to the poor. He has
sent me to pro-claim re-lease to the cap-tives and re-
cov-er-ing of sight to the blind,
to set at lib-er-ty those who are op-press-ed, to pro-
claim the ac-cept-a-ble year of the Lord.

May be sung without accompaniment, antiphonally: the leader sings a phrase, the people repeat it, and this pattern continues throughout the seven musical phrases of the song (marked*). Then all sing the song without the repeats.

108. Come follow me now

Capo 1 (E)
Anna Withey
(age 10)
Simple and unhurried
F(E)
C7(B7)
Come fol-low me now, come fol-low me now, come fol-low me
last time
B♭(A)
now, said Je - sus. 1. He died on the cross and
2. I share my bo - dy with the
F(E)
C7(B7)
F(E)
bore all our pain. I walk in his love, and he sends the
whole of the world; if you drink of my blood, you will live ev - er-
B♭(A)
F(E)
rain to wa - ter the plants that he gives to us. And
more. So fol - low me now, go tell the good news that
C7(B7)
F(E)
F(E)
last time
I do know he loves us.
Christ is liv - ing in us.
Come Je - - sus.

Topical Index

Choirmaster's Guide

The following songs are appropriate for *CHOIRS*

The following songs have verses which may be sung as *SOLOS* or by *SOLO ENSEMBLES*

Index of titles and first lines

The first line of a song is included, in italic type, only where it differs from the title